Mathematics for Christian Living Series

Progressing With Arithmetic

Grade 5 Speed Drills

Copyright, 1995
by

Rod and Staff Publishers, Inc.
P.O. Box 3, Hwy. 172,
Crockett, Kentucky 41413
Telephone: (606) 522-4348

Printed in U.S.A.

ISBN 978-07399-0472-5

Catalog no. 13571.3

12 — 20 19 18 17 16

To the Teacher

This tablet contains a speed drill for each even-numbered lesson of the Grade 5 math course.

The speed drills are designed to be used every two days. Their purpose is to develop speed and accuracy in basic mathematical skills. Each drill is numbered according to the lesson with which it should be used. The time limit for most speed drills is two minutes.

It is recommended that the teacher record grades every two or three drills, or about once a week. If grades are to be recorded, give pupils three minutes to work instead of the usual two. Allow even more time for some drills, as noted in the teacher's guide. The grade should reflect accuracy first and speed second.

For the scoring of speed drills, a number of points has been assigned to each item. The score is obtained by multiplying the number wrong times the number of points per item, and subtracting from 100.

Speed Drill 2

Name _____   **Score** _____

"Whatsoever thy hand findeth to do, do it with thy might."

(Ecclesiastes 9:10)

1.

0	1	5	0	5	2	2	3	3	8
+ 0	+ 5	+ 5	+ 8	+ 1	+ 6	+ 8	+ 7	+ 9	+ 6

2.

9	4	6	9	5	2	9	8	0	9
+ 8	+ 2	+ 7	+ 3	+ 2	+ 4	+ 4	+ 1	+ 3	+ 1

3.

7	8	0	6	9	8	6	5	9	8
+ 3	+ 4	+ 5	+ 6	+ 9	+ 2	+ 3	+ 8	+ 5	+ 7

4.

2	6	5	5	5	3	6	4	9	7
+ 9	+ 2	+ 3	+ 9	+ 4	+ 8	+ 4	+ 7	+ 6	+ 6

5.

3	2	6	3	8	8	7	4	6	9
+ 5	+ 3	+ 5	+ 4	+ 9	+ 8	+ 7	+ 1	+ 8	+ 7

2 pt. each

Speed Drill 4

Name _____   *Score* _____

"Whatsoever thy hand findeth to do, do it with thy might."

(Ecclesiastes 9:10)

1.

1	7	9	2	5	4	8	7	6	5
+ 4	+ 2	+ 9	+ 4	+ 1	+ 5	+ 0	+ 1	+ 0	+ 4

2.

3	2	5	9	3	4	7	6	9	4
+ 6	+ 9	+ 8	+ 3	+ 7	+ 8	+ 7	+ 5	+ 4	+ 7

3.

7	7	8	9	8	6	9	8	8	7
+ 5	+ 9	+ 7	+ 8	+ 6	+ 9	+ 7	+ 3	+ 5	+ 6

4.

7	7	9	6	3	5	6	4	8	9
+ 4	+ 8	+ 5	+ 7	+ 9	+ 9	+ 8	+ 9	+ 9	+ 6

5.

3	1	8	5	2	5	4	9	4	6
+ 5	+ 9	+ 2	+ 2	+ 6	+ 6	+ 1	+ 2	+ 3	+ 4

6.

3	2	5	9	3	4	7	6	9	4
+ 6	+ 9	+ 8	+ 3	+ 7	+ 8	+ 7	+ 5	+ 4	+ 7

2 pt. each

Speed Drill 6

Name _____   **Score** _____

"Whatsoever thy hand findeth to do, do it with thy might."

(Ecclesiastes 9:10)

1.

11	10	10	4	6	15	7	5	2	1
− 7	− 8	− 9	− 1	− 1	− 8	− 6	− 3	− 0	− 1

2.

0	8	14	9	7	10	14	18	14	9
− 0	− 1	− 8	− 5	− 7	− 2	− 7	− 9	− 9	− 1

3.

3	1	4	9	6	9	12	13	12	11
− 3	− 0	− 2	− 3	− 4	− 4	− 3	− 7	− 9	− 4

4.

2	5	7	10	8	13	8	17	13	13
− 1	− 5	− 0	− 1	− 5	− 4	− 6	− 9	− 5	− 6

5.

9	8	4	6	5	7	10	11	16	12
− 2	− 3	− 4	− 0	− 4	− 3	− 3	− 9	− 7	− 7

2 pt. each

Speed Drill 8

"Whatsoever thy hand findeth to do, do it with thy might."

(Ecclesiastes 9:10)

1.

| $\begin{array}{r}8\\-0\\\hline\end{array}$ | $\begin{array}{r}9\\-0\\\hline\end{array}$ | $\begin{array}{r}6\\-5\\\hline\end{array}$ | $\begin{array}{r}8\\-8\\\hline\end{array}$ | $\begin{array}{r}10\\-5\\\hline\end{array}$ | $\begin{array}{r}6\\-6\\\hline\end{array}$ | $\begin{array}{r}9\\-6\\\hline\end{array}$ | $\begin{array}{r}12\\-5\\\hline\end{array}$ | $\begin{array}{r}17\\-8\\\hline\end{array}$ | $\begin{array}{r}15\\-9\\\hline\end{array}$ |

2.

| $\begin{array}{r}6\\-3\\\hline\end{array}$ | $\begin{array}{r}3\\-2\\\hline\end{array}$ | $\begin{array}{r}5\\-0\\\hline\end{array}$ | $\begin{array}{r}9\\-9\\\hline\end{array}$ | $\begin{array}{r}9\\-7\\\hline\end{array}$ | $\begin{array}{r}14\\-5\\\hline\end{array}$ | $\begin{array}{r}9\\-8\\\hline\end{array}$ | $\begin{array}{r}12\\-4\\\hline\end{array}$ | $\begin{array}{r}11\\-6\\\hline\end{array}$ | $\begin{array}{r}15\\-7\\\hline\end{array}$ |

3.

| $\begin{array}{r}4\\-3\\\hline\end{array}$ | $\begin{array}{r}2\\-2\\\hline\end{array}$ | $\begin{array}{r}8\\-4\\\hline\end{array}$ | $\begin{array}{r}7\\-1\\\hline\end{array}$ | $\begin{array}{r}8\\-2\\\hline\end{array}$ | $\begin{array}{r}7\\-5\\\hline\end{array}$ | $\begin{array}{r}11\\-5\\\hline\end{array}$ | $\begin{array}{r}14\\-6\\\hline\end{array}$ | $\begin{array}{r}10\\-7\\\hline\end{array}$ | $\begin{array}{r}12\\-8\\\hline\end{array}$ |

4.

| $\begin{array}{r}16\\-7\\\hline\end{array}$ | $\begin{array}{r}11\\-8\\\hline\end{array}$ | $\begin{array}{r}10\\-6\\\hline\end{array}$ | $\begin{array}{r}12\\-6\\\hline\end{array}$ | $\begin{array}{r}11\\-2\\\hline\end{array}$ | $\begin{array}{r}7\\-4\\\hline\end{array}$ | $\begin{array}{r}8\\-7\\\hline\end{array}$ | $\begin{array}{r}3\\-1\\\hline\end{array}$ | $\begin{array}{r}4\\-4\\\hline\end{array}$ | $\begin{array}{r}3\\-0\\\hline\end{array}$ |

5.

| $\begin{array}{r}5\\-1\\\hline\end{array}$ | $\begin{array}{r}7\\-2\\\hline\end{array}$ | $\begin{array}{r}6\\-2\\\hline\end{array}$ | $\begin{array}{r}11\\-3\\\hline\end{array}$ | $\begin{array}{r}5\\-2\\\hline\end{array}$ | $\begin{array}{r}10\\-4\\\hline\end{array}$ | $\begin{array}{r}16\\-8\\\hline\end{array}$ | $\begin{array}{r}13\\-8\\\hline\end{array}$ | $\begin{array}{r}15\\-6\\\hline\end{array}$ | $\begin{array}{r}13\\-9\\\hline\end{array}$ |

2 pt. each

Speed Drill 10

Name _____   *Score* _____

"Whatsoever thy hand findeth to do, do it with thy might."

(Ecclesiastes 9:10)

1.

6	5	4	2	0	6	1	6	3	2
× 5	× 8	× 2	× 0	× 7	× 4	× 3	× 3	× 9	× 4

2.

4	3	1	6	5	0	5	2	3	4
× 4	× 5	× 8	× 6	× 5	× 0	× 4	× 9	× 3	× 8

3.

6	2	0	5	3	4	1	5	6	4
× 7	× 5	× 2	× 9	× 8	× 7	× 4	× 6	× 8	× 9

4.

1	3	6	4	4	5	0	6	2	5
× 1	× 2	× 9	× 6	× 3	× 7	× 8	× 2	× 7	× 3

5.

4	2	5	6	4	2	3	3	6	3
× 5	× 8	× 2	× 1	× 7	× 3	× 7	× 6	× 0	× 4

2 pt. each

Speed Drill 12

Name _____   **Score** _____

"Whatsoever thy hand findeth to do, do it with thy might."

(Ecclesiastes 9:10)

1.

| $\times\,\begin{array}{r}4\\8\end{array}$ | $\times\,\begin{array}{r}5\\5\end{array}$ | $\times\,\begin{array}{r}7\\6\end{array}$ | $\times\,\begin{array}{r}8\\3\end{array}$ | $\times\,\begin{array}{r}3\\4\end{array}$ | $\times\,\begin{array}{r}2\\3\end{array}$ | $\times\,\begin{array}{r}9\\3\end{array}$ | $\times\,\begin{array}{r}5\\4\end{array}$ | $\times\,\begin{array}{r}1\\7\end{array}$ | $\times\,\begin{array}{r}6\\8\end{array}$ |

2.

| $\times\,\begin{array}{r}8\\5\end{array}$ | $\times\,\begin{array}{r}4\\9\end{array}$ | $\times\,\begin{array}{r}2\\4\end{array}$ | $\times\,\begin{array}{r}9\\2\end{array}$ | $\times\,\begin{array}{r}7\\7\end{array}$ | $\times\,\begin{array}{r}5\\9\end{array}$ | $\times\,\begin{array}{r}7\\8\end{array}$ | $\times\,\begin{array}{r}6\\9\end{array}$ | $\times\,\begin{array}{r}8\\8\end{array}$ | $\times\,\begin{array}{r}3\\7\end{array}$ |

3.

| $\times\,\begin{array}{r}5\\6\end{array}$ | $\times\,\begin{array}{r}7\\9\end{array}$ | $\times\,\begin{array}{r}9\\9\end{array}$ | $\times\,\begin{array}{r}8\\7\end{array}$ | $\times\,\begin{array}{r}5\\7\end{array}$ | $\times\,\begin{array}{r}4\\6\end{array}$ | $\times\,\begin{array}{r}9\\8\end{array}$ | $\times\,\begin{array}{r}3\\6\end{array}$ | $\times\,\begin{array}{r}6\\6\end{array}$ | $\times\,\begin{array}{r}1\\5\end{array}$ |

4.

| $\times\,\begin{array}{r}6\\7\end{array}$ | $\times\,\begin{array}{r}4\\4\end{array}$ | $\times\,\begin{array}{r}0\\9\end{array}$ | $\times\,\begin{array}{r}3\\9\end{array}$ | $\times\,\begin{array}{r}9\\7\end{array}$ | $\times\,\begin{array}{r}7\\4\end{array}$ | $\times\,\begin{array}{r}5\\3\end{array}$ | $\times\,\begin{array}{r}8\\2\end{array}$ | $\times\,\begin{array}{r}2\\6\end{array}$ | $\times\,\begin{array}{r}8\\9\end{array}$ |

5.

| $\times\,\begin{array}{r}9\\6\end{array}$ | $\times\,\begin{array}{r}5\\8\end{array}$ | $\times\,\begin{array}{r}3\\8\end{array}$ | $\times\,\begin{array}{r}4\\7\end{array}$ | $\times\,\begin{array}{r}8\\6\end{array}$ | $\times\,\begin{array}{r}1\\1\end{array}$ | $\times\,\begin{array}{r}7\\5\end{array}$ | $\times\,\begin{array}{r}6\\4\end{array}$ | $\times\,\begin{array}{r}2\\2\end{array}$ | $\times\,\begin{array}{r}9\\5\end{array}$ |

2 pt. each

Speed Drill 14

Name _____   *Score* _____

"Whatsoever thy hand findeth to do, do it with thy might."

(Ecclesiastes 9:10)

1.
$$
\begin{array}{r} 7 \\ \times 8 \\ \hline \end{array}
\quad
\begin{array}{r} 4 \\ \times 6 \\ \hline \end{array}
\quad
\begin{array}{r} 9 \\ \times 9 \\ \hline \end{array}
\quad
\begin{array}{r} 3 \\ \times 6 \\ \hline \end{array}
\quad
\begin{array}{r} 2 \\ \times 9 \\ \hline \end{array}
\quad
\begin{array}{r} 10 \\ \times 8 \\ \hline \end{array}
\quad
\begin{array}{r} 6 \\ \times 7 \\ \hline \end{array}
\quad
\begin{array}{r} 5 \\ \times 8 \\ \hline \end{array}
\quad
\begin{array}{r} 0 \\ \times 4 \\ \hline \end{array}
\quad
\begin{array}{r} 7 \\ \times 4 \\ \hline \end{array}
$$

2.
$$
\begin{array}{r} 8 \\ \times 8 \\ \hline \end{array}
\quad
\begin{array}{r} 3 \\ \times 9 \\ \hline \end{array}
\quad
\begin{array}{r} 6 \\ \times 6 \\ \hline \end{array}
\quad
\begin{array}{r} 5 \\ \times 5 \\ \hline \end{array}
\quad
\begin{array}{r} 2 \\ \times 4 \\ \hline \end{array}
\quad
\begin{array}{r} 1 \\ \times 6 \\ \hline \end{array}
\quad
\begin{array}{r} 9 \\ \times 6 \\ \hline \end{array}
\quad
\begin{array}{r} 4 \\ \times 8 \\ \hline \end{array}
\quad
\begin{array}{r} 7 \\ \times 7 \\ \hline \end{array}
\quad
\begin{array}{r} 12 \\ \times 6 \\ \hline \end{array}
$$

3.
$$
\begin{array}{r} 9 \\ \times 8 \\ \hline \end{array}
\quad
\begin{array}{r} 11 \\ \times 4 \\ \hline \end{array}
\quad
\begin{array}{r} 8 \\ \times 6 \\ \hline \end{array}
\quad
\begin{array}{r} 7 \\ \times 5 \\ \hline \end{array}
\quad
\begin{array}{r} 3 \\ \times 8 \\ \hline \end{array}
\quad
\begin{array}{r} 7 \\ \times 9 \\ \hline \end{array}
\quad
\begin{array}{r} 10 \\ \times 6 \\ \hline \end{array}
\quad
\begin{array}{r} 5 \\ \times 6 \\ \hline \end{array}
\quad
\begin{array}{r} 9 \\ \times 4 \\ \hline \end{array}
\quad
\begin{array}{r} 12 \\ \times 4 \\ \hline \end{array}
$$

4.
$$
\begin{array}{r} 6 \\ \times 9 \\ \hline \end{array}
\quad
\begin{array}{r} 1 \\ \times 5 \\ \hline \end{array}
\quad
\begin{array}{r} 12 \\ \times 2 \\ \hline \end{array}
\quad
\begin{array}{r} 12 \\ \times 7 \\ \hline \end{array}
\quad
\begin{array}{r} 9 \\ \times 5 \\ \hline \end{array}
\quad
\begin{array}{r} 4 \\ \times 4 \\ \hline \end{array}
\quad
\begin{array}{r} 8 \\ \times 7 \\ \hline \end{array}
\quad
\begin{array}{r} 12 \\ \times 3 \\ \hline \end{array}
\quad
\begin{array}{r} 11 \\ \times 5 \\ \hline \end{array}
\quad
\begin{array}{r} 7 \\ \times 6 \\ \hline \end{array}
$$

5.
$$
\begin{array}{r} 12 \\ \times 5 \\ \hline \end{array}
\quad
\begin{array}{r} 0 \\ \times 6 \\ \hline \end{array}
\quad
\begin{array}{r} 12 \\ \times 8 \\ \hline \end{array}
\quad
\begin{array}{r} 9 \\ \times 7 \\ \hline \end{array}
\quad
\begin{array}{r} 4 \\ \times 3 \\ \hline \end{array}
\quad
\begin{array}{r} 3 \\ \times 5 \\ \hline \end{array}
\quad
\begin{array}{r} 7 \\ \times 3 \\ \hline \end{array}
\quad
\begin{array}{r} 6 \\ \times 8 \\ \hline \end{array}
\quad
\begin{array}{r} 2 \\ \times 7 \\ \hline \end{array}
\quad
\begin{array}{r} 4 \\ \times 5 \\ \hline \end{array}
$$

2 pt. each

Speed Drill 16

Name _____   *Score* _____

"Whatsoever thy hand findeth to do, do it with thy might."

(Ecclesiastes 9:10)

1.
$$\begin{array}{r} 6 \\ \times\ 6 \\ \hline \end{array}\quad \begin{array}{r} 12 \\ \times\ 3 \\ \hline \end{array}\quad \begin{array}{r} 9 \\ \times\ 4 \\ \hline \end{array}\quad \begin{array}{r} 8 \\ \times\ 5 \\ \hline \end{array}\quad \begin{array}{r} 5 \\ \times\ 9 \\ \hline \end{array}\quad \begin{array}{r} 10 \\ \times\ 4 \\ \hline \end{array}\quad \begin{array}{r} 11 \\ \times\ 7 \\ \hline \end{array}\quad \begin{array}{r} 7 \\ \times\ 9 \\ \hline \end{array}\quad \begin{array}{r} 6 \\ \times\ 3 \\ \hline \end{array}\quad \begin{array}{r} 4 \\ \times\ 5 \\ \hline \end{array}$$

2.
$$\begin{array}{r} 8 \\ \times\ 9 \\ \hline \end{array}\quad \begin{array}{r} 11 \\ \times\ 4 \\ \hline \end{array}\quad \begin{array}{r} 10 \\ \times\ 10 \\ \hline \end{array}\quad \begin{array}{r} 12 \\ \times\ 10 \\ \hline \end{array}\quad \begin{array}{r} 6 \\ \times\ 7 \\ \hline \end{array}\quad \begin{array}{r} 9 \\ \times\ 9 \\ \hline \end{array}\quad \begin{array}{r} 4 \\ \times\ 6 \\ \hline \end{array}\quad \begin{array}{r} 11 \\ \times\ 10 \\ \hline \end{array}\quad \begin{array}{r} 12 \\ \times\ 8 \\ \hline \end{array}\quad \begin{array}{r} 8 \\ \times\ 8 \\ \hline \end{array}$$

3.
$$\begin{array}{r} 6 \\ \times\ 8 \\ \hline \end{array}\quad \begin{array}{r} 12 \\ \times\ 5 \\ \hline \end{array}\quad \begin{array}{r} 9 \\ \times\ 6 \\ \hline \end{array}\quad \begin{array}{r} 4 \\ \times\ 7 \\ \hline \end{array}\quad \begin{array}{r} 11 \\ \times\ 8 \\ \hline \end{array}\quad \begin{array}{r} 12 \\ \times\ 12 \\ \hline \end{array}\quad \begin{array}{r} 11 \\ \times\ 11 \\ \hline \end{array}\quad \begin{array}{r} 7 \\ \times\ 8 \\ \hline \end{array}\quad \begin{array}{r} 5 \\ \times\ 7 \\ \hline \end{array}\quad \begin{array}{r} 3 \\ \times\ 8 \\ \hline \end{array}$$

4.
$$\begin{array}{r} 7 \\ \times\ 7 \\ \hline \end{array}\quad \begin{array}{r} 9 \\ \times\ 3 \\ \hline \end{array}\quad \begin{array}{r} 12 \\ \times\ 4 \\ \hline \end{array}\quad \begin{array}{r} 10 \\ \times\ 3 \\ \hline \end{array}\quad \begin{array}{r} 0 \\ \times\ 7 \\ \hline \end{array}\quad \begin{array}{r} 11 \\ \times\ 5 \\ \hline \end{array}\quad \begin{array}{r} 12 \\ \times\ 11 \\ \hline \end{array}\quad \begin{array}{r} 8 \\ \times\ 4 \\ \hline \end{array}\quad \begin{array}{r} 10 \\ \times\ 11 \\ \hline \end{array}\quad \begin{array}{r} 6 \\ \times\ 5 \\ \hline \end{array}$$

5.
$$\begin{array}{r} 9 \\ \times\ 7 \\ \hline \end{array}\quad \begin{array}{r} 12 \\ \times\ 9 \\ \hline \end{array}\quad \begin{array}{r} 12 \\ \times\ 7 \\ \hline \end{array}\quad \begin{array}{r} 10 \\ \times\ 3 \\ \hline \end{array}\quad \begin{array}{r} 1 \\ \times\ 2 \\ \hline \end{array}\quad \begin{array}{r} 7 \\ \times\ 3 \\ \hline \end{array}\quad \begin{array}{r} 8 \\ \times\ 6 \\ \hline \end{array}\quad \begin{array}{r} 4 \\ \times\ 4 \\ \hline \end{array}\quad \begin{array}{r} 6 \\ \times\ 9 \\ \hline \end{array}\quad \begin{array}{r} 12 \\ \times\ 3 \\ \hline \end{array}$$

2 pt. each

Speed Drill 18

Name _____   Score _____

"Whatsoever thy hand findeth to do, do it with thy might."

(Ecclesiastes 9:10)

1.

5	4	8	9	5	7
8	3	2	4	5	8
+ 7	+ 9	+ 8	+ 6	+ 6	+ 6

2.

8	5	1	3	8	7
9	9	8	6	4	7
+ 7	+ 7	+ 7	+ 9	+ 9	+ 6

3.

5	7	2	8	9	6
9	6	9	5	6	5
+ 8	+ 5	+ 6	+ 9	+ 6	+ 8

4 pt. each

Speed Drill 20

"Whatsoever thy hand findeth to do, do it with thy might."

(Ecclesiastes 9:10)

1.

8	7	5	9	3	7
8	6	9	3	7	8
6	4	7	8	4	6
+ 7	+ 5	+ 5	+ 7	+ 9	+ 2

2.

7	4	8	9	6	3
8	9	9	7	4	6
5	8	7	4	8	9
+ 7	+ 5	+ 6	+ 5	+ 7	+ 6

6 pt. each

Speed Drill 22

"Whatsoever thy hand findeth to do, do it with thy might."

(Ecclesiastes 9:10)

1. $5\overline{)15}$ $4\overline{)24}$ $3\overline{)27}$ $1\overline{)7}$ $2\overline{)14}$ $6\overline{)12}$ $4\overline{)20}$

2. $3\overline{)15}$ $1\overline{)5}$ $5\overline{)5}$ $3\overline{)12}$ $4\overline{)28}$ $3\overline{)6}$ $2\overline{)0}$

3. $4\overline{)16}$ $6\overline{)18}$ $5\overline{)25}$ $3\overline{)9}$ $6\overline{)36}$ $5\overline{)45}$ $2\overline{)18}$

4. $3\overline{)0}$ $2\overline{)6}$ $3\overline{)21}$ $4\overline{)32}$ $2\overline{)8}$ $6\overline{)6}$ $6\overline{)24}$

5. $6\overline{)30}$ $3\overline{)24}$ $4\overline{)8}$ $2\overline{)4}$ $5\overline{)20}$ $6\overline{)48}$ $5\overline{)10}$

6. $4\overline{)36}$ $5\overline{)40}$ $2\overline{)10}$ $6\overline{)54}$ $3\overline{)21}$ $4\overline{)12}$ $5\overline{)30}$

7. $6\overline{)42}$ $4\overline{)32}$ $3\overline{)3}$ $5\overline{)35}$ $6\overline{)24}$ $3\overline{)18}$ $2\overline{)16}$

2 pt. each

Speed Drill 24

Name _____   **Score** _____

"Whatsoever thy hand findeth to do, do it with thy might."

(Ecclesiastes 9:10)

1. $6\overline{)36}$ $7\overline{)42}$ $4\overline{)28}$ $5\overline{)20}$ $8\overline{)16}$ $4\overline{)12}$ $8\overline{)64}$

2. $5\overline{)30}$ $8\overline{)24}$ $7\overline{)35}$ $4\overline{)16}$ $2\overline{)18}$ $7\overline{)56}$ $4\overline{)36}$

3. $8\overline{)0}$ $8\overline{)72}$ $3\overline{)27}$ $5\overline{)25}$ $4\overline{)20}$ $9\overline{)81}$ $9\overline{)27}$

4. $7\overline{)49}$ $7\overline{)63}$ $3\overline{)24}$ $2\overline{)12}$ $5\overline{)35}$ $9\overline{)45}$ $8\overline{)48}$

5. $6\overline{)42}$ $4\overline{)24}$ $6\overline{)30}$ $6\overline{)18}$ $9\overline{)18}$ $8\overline{)32}$ $7\overline{)28}$

6. $4\overline{)8}$ $9\overline{)36}$ $6\overline{)48}$ $5\overline{)15}$ $7\overline{)7}$ $9\overline{)54}$ $4\overline{)32}$

7. $6\overline{)54}$ $4\overline{)36}$ $3\overline{)18}$ $3\overline{)21}$ $9\overline{)72}$ $7\overline{)63}$ $8\overline{)56}$

2 pt. each

Speed Drill 26

"Whatsoever thy hand findeth to do, do it with thy might."

(Ecclesiastes 9:10)

1.

46	83	59	67	36
25	59	65	77	89
+ 57	+ 14	+ 74	+ 38	+ 82

2.

8,843	3,927	74,589	49,765
+ 1,697	+ 9,875	+ 89,546	+ 39,642

8 pt. each

Speed Drill 28

Name _____   **Score** _____

"Whatsoever thy hand findeth to do, do it with thy might."

(Ecclesiastes 9:10)

1.

$$\begin{array}{r} 700 \\ -386 \\ \hline \end{array}$$
$$\begin{array}{r} 603 \\ -457 \\ \hline \end{array}$$
$$\begin{array}{r} 820 \\ -362 \\ \hline \end{array}$$
$$\begin{array}{r} 935 \\ -893 \\ \hline \end{array}$$
$$\begin{array}{r} 642 \\ -148 \\ \hline \end{array}$$

2.

$$\begin{array}{r} 8{,}030 \\ -5{,}439 \\ \hline \end{array}$$
$$\begin{array}{r} 6{,}000 \\ -4{,}562 \\ \hline \end{array}$$
$$\begin{array}{r} 5{,}173 \\ -3{,}645 \\ \hline \end{array}$$
$$\begin{array}{r} 9{,}628 \\ -6{,}549 \\ \hline \end{array}$$
$$\begin{array}{r} 7{,}400 \\ -5{,}690 \\ \hline \end{array}$$

8 pt. each

Speed Drill 30

Name _____   Score _____

"Whatsoever thy hand findeth to do, do it with thy might."

(Ecclesiastes 9:10)

1.

8	9	6	7	4	3	8	6	3	7
× 6	× 4	× 3	× 3	× 4	× 9	× 8	× 7	× 4	× 7

2.

5	3	10	8	5	7	5	1	4	2
× 7	× 8	× 9	× 7	× 4	× 9	× 3	× 9	× 8	× 5

3.

8	9	7	5	12	8	2	6	12	9
× 5	× 9	× 4	× 6	× 4	× 9	× 7	× 6	× 2	× 6

4.

5	2	12	10	9	10	12	12	8	11
× 9	× 6	× 7	× 6	× 3	× 10	× 8	× 12	× 6	× 11

5.

4	12	10	10	6	3	2	11	12	7
× 6	× 3	× 11	× 8	× 9	× 7	× 4	× 12	× 9	× 8

6.

6	11	12	7	5	8	9	12	10	12
× 3	× 6	× 11	× 6	× 8	× 3	× 7	× 5	× 12	× 6

2 pt. each

Speed Drill 32

Name _____   **Score** _____

"Whatsoever thy hand findeth to do, do it with thy might."

(Ecclesiastes 9:10)

1.

$$\begin{array}{r} 684 \\ \times\ 4 \\ \hline \end{array}$$
$$\begin{array}{r} 937 \\ \times\ 3 \\ \hline \end{array}$$
$$\begin{array}{r} 845 \\ \times\ 5 \\ \hline \end{array}$$
$$\begin{array}{r} 286 \\ \times\ 6 \\ \hline \end{array}$$
$$\begin{array}{r} 193 \\ \times\ 8 \\ \hline \end{array}$$

2.

$$\begin{array}{r} 60 \\ \times\ 37 \\ \hline \end{array}$$
$$\begin{array}{r} 27 \\ \times\ 54 \\ \hline \end{array}$$
$$\begin{array}{r} 46 \\ \times\ 18 \\ \hline \end{array}$$
$$\begin{array}{r} 39 \\ \times\ 92 \\ \hline \end{array}$$

8 pt. each

Speed Drill 34

Name _____   Score _____

"Whatsoever thy hand findeth to do, do it with thy might."

(Ecclesiastes 9:10)

Match the numbers to the number words.

_____ **1.** one hundred two billion

_____ **2.** one hundred two million

_____ **3.** one hundred ten million, one hundred two thousand

_____ **4.** one hundred one million, twelve thousand

_____ **5.** one hundred twenty billion, twenty thousand, ten

_____ **6.** one hundred twenty million, twenty thousand, ten

_____ **7.** twelve billion, twenty million, one hundred twenty thousand

_____ **8.** twelve million, one hundred twenty thousand, ten

_____ **9.** one hundred billion, one hundred twenty thousand

_____ **10.** one hundred billion, one hundred twenty

a. 102,000,000

b. 101,012,000

c. 120,020,010

d. 102,000,000,000

e. 100,000,120,000

f. 12,120,010

g. 12,020,120,000

h. 120,000,020,010

i. 100,000,000,120

j. 110,102,000

8 pt. each

Speed Drill 36

Name _____   **Score** _____

"Whatsoever thy hand findeth to do, do it with thy might."

(Ecclesiastes 9:10)

1.   5)375   6)1,482   9)675   4)656

2.   3)5,784   2)7,450   8)9,464

9 pt. each

Speed Drill 38

"Whatsoever thy hand findeth to do, do it with thy might."

(Ecclesiastes 9:10)

1.

4	8	7	9	6	5
6	9	7	6	5	7
5	2	3	4	8	7
+ 8	+ 9	+ 6	+ 5	+ 8	+ 4

2.

8	6	4	7	3	9
8	6	7	9	6	4
4	7	9	5	6	3
+ 5	+ 6	+ 2	+ 5	+ 8	+ 5

6 pt. each

Speed Drill 40

"Whatsoever thy hand findeth to do, do it with thy might."

(Ecclesiastes 9:10)

1. 1 yard = _____ feet   1 foot = _____ inches   1 mile = _____ feet

2. 1 quart = _____ cups   1 quart = _____ pints   1 gallon = _____ quarts

3. 1 pint = _____ cups   1 peck = _____ quarts   1 mile = _____ yards

4. 1 year = _____ days   1 bushel = _____ pecks   1 year = _____ months

5. 1 year = _____ weeks   1 decade = _____ years   1 leap year = _____ days

6. 1 week = _____ days   1 ton = _____ pounds   1 pound = _____ ounces

7. 1 day = _____ hours   1 hour = _____ minutes   1 century = _____ years

8. 1 dozen = _____ eggs   1 yard = _____ inches   1 minute = _____ seconds

4 pt. each

Speed Drill 42

"Whatsoever thy hand findeth to do, do it with thy might."

(Ecclesiastes 9:10)

1.

8	5	8	9	6	4	7	9	5	3
− 5	− 4	− 8	− 2	− 4	− 4	− 0	− 5	− 3	− 1

2.

9	10	11	8	7	12	10	9	6	16
− 3	− 5	− 8	− 4	− 6	− 9	− 4	− 8	− 3	− 7

3.

7	11	14	15	17	8	9	10	12	9
− 5	− 5	− 6	− 9	− 8	− 6	− 6	− 7	− 6	− 4

4.

6	7	10	15	9	5	6	11	13	16
− 2	− 4	− 6	− 8	− 1	− 3	− 5	− 9	− 5	− 8

5.

8	13	12	17	10	7	13	14	16	11
− 7	− 7	− 8	− 9	− 9	− 3	− 9	− 7	− 9	− 7

6.

14	11	15	18	10	12	12	11	13	14
− 9	− 3	− 6	− 9	− 2	− 7	− 4	− 6	− 4	− 8

2 pt. each

Speed Drill 44

Name _____   **Score** _____

"Whatsoever thy hand findeth to do, do it with thy might."

(Ecclesiastes 9:10)

1.

590	733	804	718	925
- 275	- 486	- 567	- 627	- 328

2.

7,000	5,020	9,800	6,472	8,305
- 5,904	- 3,519	- 2,687	- 4,573	- 7,647

8 pt. each

Speed Drill 46

Name _____   **Score** _____

"Whatsoever thy hand findeth to do, do it with thy might."

(Ecclesiastes 9:10)

1. 16 + 7 = _____   18 – 7 = _____   3 × 50 = _____

2. 35 + 6 = _____   25 – 5 = _____   8 × 70 = _____

3. 27 + 8 = _____   38 – 4 = _____   5 × 12 = _____

4. 14 + 9 = _____   20 – 5 = _____   4 × 60 = _____

5. 47 + 4 = _____   31 – 3 = _____   6 × 30 = _____

6. 23 + 7 = _____   24 – 2 = _____   10 × 17 = _____

7. 15 + 8 = _____   37 – 4 = _____   25 × 10 = _____

4 pt. each

Speed Drill 48

"Whatsoever thy hand findeth to do, do it with thy might."

(Ecclesiastes 9:10)

1. $\frac{1}{3}$ of 24 = _____ $\frac{2}{3}$ of 24 = _____

2. $\frac{1}{2}$ of 18 = _____ $\frac{3}{4}$ of 8 = _____

3. $\frac{1}{5}$ of 35 = _____ $\frac{3}{5}$ of 35 = _____

4. $\frac{1}{4}$ of 20 = _____ $\frac{3}{4}$ of 20 = _____

5. $\frac{1}{7}$ of 14 = _____ $\frac{2}{7}$ of 14 = _____

6. $\frac{1}{9}$ of 72 = _____ $\frac{4}{9}$ of 72 = _____

7. $\frac{1}{6}$ of 36 = _____ $\frac{5}{6}$ of 36 = _____

8. $\frac{1}{8}$ of 24 = _____ $\frac{5}{8}$ of 24 = _____

9. $\frac{1}{2}$ of 2 = _____ $\frac{7}{8}$ of 24 = _____

10. $\frac{1}{10}$ of 50 = _____ $\frac{3}{10}$ of 50 = _____

5 pt. each

Speed Drill 50

Name _____   **Score** _____

A. *Write* P, I, *or* M *for* proper fraction, improper fraction, *or* mixed number.

1. $\frac{3}{2}$ _____ $\frac{2}{3}$ _____ $1\frac{1}{2}$ _____

B. *Match the terms with the numbers in the problems by writing the correct letters in the blanks. Some blanks will get two letters.*

2. _____ numerator
3. _____ difference
4. _____ subtrahend
5. _____ sum
6. _____ multiplicand
7. _____ denominator
8. _____ partial product
9. _____ quotient
10. _____ multiplier
11. _____ divisor
12. _____ product
13. _____ minuend
14. _____ dividend
15. _____ addend
16. _____ remainder

a.   35
b. + 78
c. 113

d.   482
e. − 187
f.   295

g. → 12 R 2 i.
h. 7)86 ← j.

k.   37
l. × 23
m. 111
n.   74
o. 851

p. $\frac{7}{8}$
q.

5 pt. each

Speed Drill 52

Name _____   Score _____

"Whatsoever thy hand findeth to do, do it with thy might."

(Ecclesiastes 9:10)

A. Write each price in two ways.

1. six cents _____ _____   six dollars _____ _____

B. Write this price, using a dollar sign and decimal point.

2. twenty-nine dollars and eighty cents _____

C. Write the numbers that fit in the blanks.

3. six dimes = _____ ¢   eleven dimes = $ _____

4. two quarters = _____ ¢   six nickels = _____ ¢

5. seven nickels = _____ ¢   seven quarters = $ _____

6. twelve pennies = _____ ¢   one half dollar = _____ ¢

7. four quarters = _____ ¢   twelve nickels = _____ ¢

6 pt. each

Speed Drill 54

Name _____   **Score** _____

"Whatsoever thy hand findeth to do, do it with thy might."

(Ecclesiastes 9:10)

Write the value of each set.

1. 5 five-dollar bills _____

2. 4 ten-dollar bills _____

3. 3 twenty-dollar bills _____

4. 2 ten-dollar bills, 4 one-dollar bills _____

5. 2 quarters, 3 dimes _____

6. 4 dimes, 6 nickels _____

7. 1 quarter, 1 dime, 1 nickel _____

8. 3 nickels, 1 dime _____

9. 3 quarters, 2 nickels, 1 dime _____

10. 5 dimes, 3 nickels, 7 pennies _____

8 pt. each

Speed Drill 56

"Whatsoever thy hand findeth to do, do it with thy might."

(Ecclesiastes 9:10)

Reduce these fractions to lowest terms.

1. $\frac{4}{8}$ $\frac{2}{10}$ $\frac{12}{16}$ $\frac{8}{20}$ $\frac{3}{12}$ $\frac{2}{8}$

2. $\frac{6}{16}$ $\frac{3}{9}$ $\frac{5}{10}$ $\frac{9}{12}$ $\frac{3}{15}$ $\frac{10}{20}$

3. $\frac{6}{9}$ $\frac{8}{12}$ $\frac{6}{8}$ $\frac{4}{6}$ $\frac{8}{16}$ $\frac{5}{30}$

5 pt. each

Speed Drill 58

"Whatsoever thy hand findeth to do, do it with thy might."

(Ecclesiastes 9:10)

Follow the signs. Write answers in simplest form.

1. $\dfrac{5}{8}$ $\dfrac{3}{4}$ $\dfrac{4}{5}$ $\dfrac{7}{10}$
    $+\dfrac{3}{8}$ $+\dfrac{3}{4}$ $+\dfrac{3}{5}$ $+\dfrac{1}{10}$

2. $\dfrac{11}{12}$ $\dfrac{13}{16}$ $\dfrac{7}{8}$ $\dfrac{8}{9}$
    $-\dfrac{5}{12}$ $-\dfrac{9}{16}$ $-\dfrac{1}{8}$ $-\dfrac{2}{9}$

10 pt. each

Speed Drill 60

Name _____   **Score** _____

"Whatsoever thy hand findeth to do, do it with thy might."

(Ecclesiastes 9:10)

A. *Write the answers in the blanks.*

1. $10 \times 75 =$ _____ $100 \times 75 =$ _____ $1{,}000 \times 75 =$ _____

2. $10 \times 28 =$ _____ $100 \times 28 =$ _____ $1{,}000 \times 28 =$ _____

3. $10 \times 41 =$ _____ $100 \times 41 =$ _____ $1{,}000 \times 41 =$ _____

B. *Round to the nearest ten.*

4. 47 _____   359 _____   2,834 _____

C. *Round to the nearest hundred.*

5. 359 _____   2,834 _____   71,648 _____

D. *Round to the nearest thousand.*

6. 2,834 _____   71,648 _____   529,350 _____

5 pt. each

Speed Drill 62

Name _____   Score _____

"Whatsoever thy hand findeth to do, do it with thy might."

(Ecclesiastes 9:10)

A. *Write two addition and two subtraction facts, using 11, 7, and 4.*

1. _____   _____   _____   _____

B. *Write two addition and two subtraction facts, using 6, 9, and 15.*

2. _____   _____   _____   _____

C. *Fill in the missing numbers.*

3. ____ + 6 = 10   8 + ____ = 14   3 + 9 = ____

4. 5 + ____ = 13   ____ + 4 = 9   7 + ____ = 12

5. 10 – ____ = 7   ____ – 6 = 6   9 – ____ = 2

6. 15 – 8 = ____   13 – ____ = 9   ____ – 8 = 3

5 pt. each

Speed Drill 64

Name _____   **Score** _____

"Whatsoever thy hand findeth to do, do it with thy might."

(Ecclesiastes 9:10)

1.

7	5	1	8	2	3	9	10	4	12
× 5	× 9	× 4	× 3	× 7	× 6	× 8	× 10	× 6	× 5

2.

6	4	9	11	12	7	3	9	6	8
× 8	× 7	× 9	× 7	× 4	× 7	× 5	× 7	× 6	× 4

3.

7	4	3	0	11	9	12	12	8	6
× 3	× 4	× 9	× 6	× 11	× 4	× 2	× 7	× 8	× 7

4.

5	12	6	8	7	5	4	11	9	10
× 4	× 3	× 9	× 5	× 8	× 5	× 8	× 10	× 2	× 12

5.

7	5	3	12	10	12	8	2	12	11
× 6	× 6	× 3	× 9	× 8	× 12	× 6	× 5	× 6	× 12

6.

6	4	0	11	7	9	12	5	3	8
× 2	× 3	× 8	× 4	× 9	× 6	× 8	× 1	× 2	× 9

2 pt. each

Speed Drill 66

Name _____   **Score** _____

"Whatsoever thy hand findeth to do, do it with thy might."

(Ecclesiastes 9:10)

Fill in the missing numbers on this multiplication table.

×	3	5	8	2	9	11	4	10	7	6	12
4						44					
7				14				70			
8							32				
5			40						35		
9		45						90			
6				12			24				
1	3								7		12
11		55			99					66	

2 pt. each

Speed Drill 68

Name _____   **Score** _____

"Whatsoever thy hand findeth to do, do it with thy might."

(Ecclesiastes 9:10)

1. $6\overline{)18}$ $3\overline{)24}$ $8\overline{)56}$ $9\overline{)36}$ $2\overline{)12}$ $7\overline{)49}$ $4\overline{)20}$

2. $7\overline{)63}$ $9\overline{)90}$ $4\overline{)24}$ $6\overline{)48}$ $8\overline{)16}$ $4\overline{)8}$ $5\overline{)30}$

3. $8\overline{)64}$ $6\overline{)36}$ $5\overline{)45}$ $5\overline{)15}$ $3\overline{)27}$ $9\overline{)81}$ $4\overline{)16}$

4. $9\overline{)72}$ $3\overline{)21}$ $5\overline{)20}$ $8\overline{)32}$ $4\overline{)28}$ $9\overline{)54}$ $3\overline{)18}$

5. $7\overline{)42}$ $5\overline{)40}$ $6\overline{)54}$ $5\overline{)25}$ $3\overline{)6}$ $2\overline{)18}$ $6\overline{)24}$

6. $9\overline{)27}$ $4\overline{)36}$ $8\overline{)48}$ $2\overline{)2}$ $4\overline{)48}$ $5\overline{)60}$ $3\overline{)33}$

7. $8\overline{)64}$ $7\overline{)56}$ $6\overline{)42}$ $5\overline{)35}$ $4\overline{)32}$ $6\overline{)60}$ $6\overline{)72}$

2 pt. each

Speed Drill 70

Name _____   *Score* _____

"Whatsoever thy hand findeth to do, do it with thy might."

(Ecclesiastes 9:10)

1. $16 \div 8 = \underline{\hspace{1cm}}$	$28 \div 7 = \underline{\hspace{1cm}}$	$35 \div 5 = \underline{\hspace{1cm}}$	$54 \div 9 = \underline{\hspace{1cm}}$
2. $30 \div 5 = \underline{\hspace{1cm}}$	$36 \div 6 = \underline{\hspace{1cm}}$	$72 \div 8 = \underline{\hspace{1cm}}$	$21 \div 3 = \underline{\hspace{1cm}}$
3. $18 \div 6 = \underline{\hspace{1cm}}$	$42 \div 6 = \underline{\hspace{1cm}}$	$56 \div 8 = \underline{\hspace{1cm}}$	$81 \div 9 = \underline{\hspace{1cm}}$
4. $50 \div 5 = \underline{\hspace{1cm}}$	$63 \div 9 = \underline{\hspace{1cm}}$	$48 \div 6 = \underline{\hspace{1cm}}$	$24 \div 3 = \underline{\hspace{1cm}}$
5. $36 \div 9 = \underline{\hspace{1cm}}$	$64 \div 8 = \underline{\hspace{1cm}}$	$40 \div 5 = \underline{\hspace{1cm}}$	$20 \div 4 = \underline{\hspace{1cm}}$
6. $16 \div 4 = \underline{\hspace{1cm}}$	$8 \div 2 = \underline{\hspace{1cm}}$	$42 \div 7 = \underline{\hspace{1cm}}$	$28 \div 4 = \underline{\hspace{1cm}}$
7. $32 \div 8 = \underline{\hspace{1cm}}$	$10 \div 5 = \underline{\hspace{1cm}}$	$49 \div 7 = \underline{\hspace{1cm}}$	$12 \div 3 = \underline{\hspace{1cm}}$
8. $18 \div 2 = \underline{\hspace{1cm}}$	$72 \div 9 = \underline{\hspace{1cm}}$	$25 \div 5 = \underline{\hspace{1cm}}$	$9 \div 3 = \underline{\hspace{1cm}}$
9. $7 \div 7 = \underline{\hspace{1cm}}$	$54 \div 6 = \underline{\hspace{1cm}}$	$45 \div 5 = \underline{\hspace{1cm}}$	$40 \div 8 = \underline{\hspace{1cm}}$
10. $24 \div 6 = \underline{\hspace{1cm}}$	$36 \div 3 = \underline{\hspace{1cm}}$	$27 \div 3 = \underline{\hspace{1cm}}$	$66 \div 6 = \underline{\hspace{1cm}}$

2 pt. each

Speed Drill 72

Name _____   Score _____

"Whatsoever thy hand findeth to do, do it with thy might."

(Ecclesiastes 9:10)

A. *Write two multiplication and two division facts, using 4, 9, and 36.*

1. _____   _____   _____   _____

B. *Write two multiplication and two division facts, using 10, 5, and 2.*

2. _____   _____   _____   _____

C. *Fill in the missing numbers.*

3. $6 \times$ ____ $= 36$ ____ $\times 7 = 28$ $12 \times 2 =$ ____

4. ____ $\times 8 = 32$ $5 \times$ ____ $= 40$ ____ $\times 6 = 12$

5. $24 \div$ ____ $= 8$ ____ $\div 5 = 5$ $56 \div$ ____ $= 7$

6. $6 \div 6 =$ ____   ____ $\div 7 = 7$ ____ $\div 9 = 8$

5 pt. each

Speed Drill 74

Name _____   **Score** _____

"Whatsoever thy hand findeth to do, do it with thy might."

(Ecclesiastes 9:10)

A. *Place commas correctly in these numbers.*

1. 8903452   41009287   29715   1972548630

B. *Follow the directions.*

2. Circle the digit in hundred thousands' place.   320,471,264

3. Circle the 8 that means 8 million.   8,888,888,888

4. Write the number that means 8,000 + 200 + 70 + 3   _____

C. *Write numerals for these number words.*

5. twenty-five million _____

6. six hundred thirty billion _____

7. three billion, three million, three thousand, three _____

10 pt. each

Speed Drill 76

Name _____ **Score** _____

"Whatsoever thy hand findeth to do, do it with thy might."

(Ecclesiastes 9:10)

A. Write the missing numbers.

1.   1 yard = _____ feet   1 yard = _____ inches   1 foot = _____ inches

2. $\frac{1}{2}$ foot = _____ inches   6 feet = _____ yards   6 yards = _____ feet

B. Write the measurements to which the arrows point.

3.   a. _____   b. _____   c. _____   d. _____   e. _____

8 pt. each

Speed Drill 78

Name _____   Score _____

"Whatsoever thy hand findeth to do, do it with thy might."

(Ecclesiastes 9:10)

A. *Write the Arabic numerals for these Roman numerals.*

1. I ____ V ____ X ____ L ____ C ____ D ____ M ____

2. IV ____ XI ____ XL ____ LX ____ CCC ____ CXX____

B. *Write the Roman numerals for these Arabic numerals.*

3. 6 _____ 9 _____ 15 _____ 27 _____ 30 _____

4. 88 _____ 90 _____ 150 _____ 400 _____ 2,000 _____

4 pt. each

Speed Drill 80

Name _____   **Score** _____

1.

8	10	12	9	7	6	12	14	3
$\times 7$	$\times 10$	$- 7$	$+ 5$	$\times 6$	$+ 8$	$\times 5$	$- 5$	$+ 8$

2.

9	12	11	16	4	8	7	11	10
$+ 8$	$\times 12$	$- 9$	$- 7$	$\times 8$	$+ 7$	$\times 9$	$\times 11$	$- 6$

3.

6	10	7	6	9	12	12	15	3
$\times 9$	$\times 11$	$+ 6$	$\times 5$	$\times 9$	$\times 8$	$- 4$	$- 6$	$\times 9$

4. $56 \div 7 =$ _____ $84 \div 12 =$ _____ $100 \div 10 =$ _____ $42 \div 6 =$ _____

5. $18 \div 3 =$ _____ $28 \div 7 =$ _____ $35 \div 5 =$ _____ $132 \div 11 =$ _____

6. 15 + 14 = _____   16 + 30 = _____   21 + 9 = _____   18 + 12 = _____   25 + 16 = _____

7. 18 – 5 = _____   23 – 10 = _____   27 – 12 = _____   25 – 7 = _____   32 – 6 = _____

8. 10 × 48 = _____   100 × 30 = _____   1,000 × 12 = _____   40 × 7 = _____   9 × 80 = _____

9. $\frac{1}{3}$ of 36 = _____ $\frac{2}{5}$ of 20 = _____ $\frac{3}{8}$ of 64 = _____ $1\frac{1}{2}$ × 14 = _____ $2\frac{1}{3}$ × 6 = _____

10. 1 ÷ 6 = _____   3 ÷ 7 = _____   2 ÷ 8 = _____   4 is what part of 12? _____

11. 1 yr. = _____ days   1 yr. = _____ wk.   1 century = _____ yr.

12. 1 mi. = _____ ft.   1 bu. = _____ pk.   1 ton = _____ lb.

13. 1 lb. = _____ oz.   1 qt. = _____ cups   1 gal. = _____ qt.

14. 1 yd. = _____ in.   1 doz. = _____ items   1 qt. = _____ pt.

15. 1 pk. = _____ qt.   1 hr. = _____ min.   1 day = _____ hr.

16. 6 ft. = _____ in.   6 ft. = _____ yd.   3 wk. = _____ days

17. 8 cups = _____ pt.   5 pt. = _____ qt.   6 mo. = _____ yr.

18. What is the lowest common denominator for each fraction pair?

a. $\frac{1}{2}$ $\frac{2}{3}$ _____   b. $\frac{3}{4}$ $\frac{7}{16}$ _____   c. $\frac{11}{12}$ $\frac{1}{2}$ _____   d. $\frac{3}{5}$ $\frac{1}{3}$ _____   e. $\frac{5}{6}$ $\frac{7}{8}$ _____

1 pt. each

Speed Drill 82

Name _____   Score _____

"Whatsoever thy hand findeth to do, do it with thy might."

(Ecclesiastes 9:10)

1.

```
            48                    641
      69    25                    577
853   36    17    5,983         + 364
+649  +45  +62   +2,834
```

2.

```
 93
 27   844   7,219   4,380
 46   349   6,473   6,228
+58  +575  +8,356  +7,691
```

8 pt. each

Speed Drill 84

Name _____   Score _____

"Whatsoever thy hand findeth to do, do it with thy might."

(Ecclesiastes 9:10)

1.

300	702	920	647	853
− 267	− 589	− 327	− 128	− 553

2.

7,000	6,031	8,506	5,080
− 3,408	− 4,269	− 8,360	− 2,543

8 pt. each

Speed Drill 86

Name _____   **Score** _____

"Whatsoever thy hand findeth to do, do it with thy might."

(Ecclesiastes 9:10)

1.

$$\begin{array}{r} 283 \\ \times\ \ 6 \\ \hline \end{array}$$
$$\begin{array}{r} 450 \\ \times\ \ 4 \\ \hline \end{array}$$
$$\begin{array}{r} 608 \\ \times\ \ 7 \\ \hline \end{array}$$
$$\begin{array}{r} 749 \\ \times\ \ 3 \\ \hline \end{array}$$

2.

$$\begin{array}{r} 60 \\ \times\ 69 \\ \hline \end{array}$$
$$\begin{array}{r} 83 \\ \times\ 52 \\ \hline \end{array}$$
$$\begin{array}{r} 15 \\ \times\ 76 \\ \hline \end{array}$$
$$\begin{array}{r} 96 \\ \times\ 34 \\ \hline \end{array}$$

8 pt. each

Speed Drill 88

Name _____   **Score** _____

"Whatsoever thy hand findeth to do, do it with thy might."

(Ecclesiastes 9:10)

1. $4\overline{)17}$ $6\overline{)34}$ $3\overline{)20}$ $5\overline{)38}$

2. $2\overline{)11}$ $8\overline{)18}$ $9\overline{)49}$ $7\overline{)52}$

3. $5\overline{)23}$ $4\overline{)30}$ $7\overline{)36}$ $6\overline{)53}$

7 pt. each

Speed Drill 90

Name _____   Score _____

"Whatsoever thy hand findeth to do, do it with thy might."

(Ecclesiastes 9:10)

1. $3\overline{)48}$ $5\overline{)65}$ $2\overline{)76}$ $6\overline{)84}$

2. $8\overline{)272}$ $3\overline{)168}$ $4\overline{)156}$ $9\overline{)477}$

8 pt. each

Speed Drill 92

Name _____   Score _____

"Whatsoever thy hand findeth to do, do it with thy might."

(Ecclesiastes 9:10)

Solve these problems. Do your work in the space at the right.

1. Sister Dorcas makes boys' shirts to send to Honduras. She uses five buttons for each shirt. If Sister Dorcas has 100 buttons, she has enough buttons for _____ shirts.

2. One month Sister Dorcas sewed 24 blue shirts and 8 white shirts. How many shirts did Sister Dorcas make that month? _____

3. Brother Wenger started his own machine shop in 1965. In 1983 he sold the business and moved his family to a mission in Honduras. How long did Brother Wenger have the machine shop? _____

4. The men at Wenger's Machine shop make metal egg carts. They need to weld 32 rivets for each cart. How many rivets need to be welded for 8 carts? _____

20 pt. each

Speed Drill 94

Name _____   Score _____

"Whatsoever thy hand findeth to do, do it with thy might."

(Ecclesiastes 9:10)

A. Reduce to lowest terms.

1. $\frac{12}{24}$ $\frac{15}{20}$ $\frac{8}{12}$ $\frac{12}{15}$ $\frac{6}{18}$

B. Change to whole or mixed numbers in simplest form.

2. $\frac{4}{3}$ $\frac{10}{2}$ $\frac{15}{10}$ $\frac{11}{4}$ $\frac{14}{6}$

C. Write the lowest common denominator for each set of fractions.

3. $\frac{4}{5}$ $\frac{1}{2}$ $\frac{5}{8}$ $\frac{1}{4}$ $\frac{9}{16}$ $\frac{1}{5}$ $\frac{5}{10}$ $\frac{2}{3}$ $\frac{1}{3}$ $\frac{3}{4}$ $\frac{1}{2}$

6 pt. each

Speed Drill 96

Name _____ **Score** _____

"Whatsoever thy hand findeth to do, do it with thy might."

(Ecclesiastes 9:10)

Follow the signs. Write the answers in simplest form.

1.
$$\frac{2}{3}$$
$$+\ \frac{1}{4}$$

$$\frac{1}{2}$$
$$+\ \frac{7}{8}$$

$$\frac{9}{16}$$
$$+\ \frac{3}{4}$$

$$\frac{3}{5}$$
$$+\ \frac{1}{2}$$

2.
$$\frac{11}{12}$$
$$-\ \frac{3}{4}$$

$$\frac{7}{10}$$
$$-\ \frac{1}{5}$$

$$\frac{1}{2}$$
$$-\ \frac{1}{3}$$

$$\frac{7}{8}$$
$$-\ \frac{3}{16}$$

8 pt. each

Speed Drill 98

Name _____   *Score* _____

"Whatsoever thy hand findeth to do, do it with thy might."

(Ecclesiastes 9:10)

Do each step in the order given.

1. $6 \times 3 \div 2 \times 8 - 6 \div 6 =$ _____

2. $4 + 7 \times 4 + 5 \div 7 \times 8 =$ _____

3. $3 \times 4 \times 5 \div 10 - 2 \times 7 - 13 =$ _____

4. $8 + 5 - 7 \times 8 - 12 \div 9 =$ _____

5. $9 - 6 \times 7 - 5 \div 2 \times 8 + 15 =$ _____

6. $12 \div 6 \div 2 \times 4 \times 8 - 3 - 5 \div 6 =$ _____

11 pt. each

Speed Drill 100

Name _____   **Score** _____

"Whatsoever thy hand findeth to do, do it with thy might."

(Ecclesiastes 9:10)

1.

5	7	2	9	6	1
3	8	9	5	3	4
8	1	9	4	7	6
3	4	5	8	7	4
+ 5	+ 8	+ 5	+ 2	+ 1	+ 5

2.

8	3	7	5	9	7
4	4	6	1	1	9
9	3	5	6	7	4
2	8	1	3	6	5
+ 5	+ 7	+ 4	+ 8	+ 3	+ 7

6 pt. each

Speed Drill 102

Name _____   *Score* _____

| 1. | $\begin{array}{r} 6 \\ \times\,7 \\ \hline \end{array}$ | $\begin{array}{r} 8 \\ +\,5 \\ \hline \end{array}$ | $\begin{array}{r} 12 \\ -\,9 \\ \hline \end{array}$ | $\begin{array}{r} 9 \\ \times\,5 \\ \hline \end{array}$ | $\begin{array}{r} 3 \\ \times\,8 \\ \hline \end{array}$ | $\begin{array}{r} 10 \\ -\,4 \\ \hline \end{array}$ | $\begin{array}{r} 7 \\ -\,7 \\ \hline \end{array}$ | $\begin{array}{r} 4 \\ \times\,9 \\ \hline \end{array}$ | $\begin{array}{r} 0 \\ +\,5 \\ \hline \end{array}$ |

| 2. | $\begin{array}{r} 4 \\ +\,7 \\ \hline \end{array}$ | $\begin{array}{r} 11 \\ \times\,11 \\ \hline \end{array}$ | $\begin{array}{r} 10 \\ \times\,10 \\ \hline \end{array}$ | $\begin{array}{r} 8 \\ \times\,9 \\ \hline \end{array}$ | $\begin{array}{r} 3 \\ +\,7 \\ \hline \end{array}$ | $\begin{array}{r} 1 \\ +\,8 \\ \hline \end{array}$ | $\begin{array}{r} 8 \\ -\,6 \\ \hline \end{array}$ | $\begin{array}{r} 9 \\ \times\,7 \\ \hline \end{array}$ | $\begin{array}{r} 12 \\ -\,5 \\ \hline \end{array}$ |

| 3. | $\begin{array}{r} 6 \\ \times\,6 \\ \hline \end{array}$ | $\begin{array}{r} 3 \\ \times\,5 \\ \hline \end{array}$ | $\begin{array}{r} 7 \\ +\,9 \\ \hline \end{array}$ | $\begin{array}{r} 10 \\ -\,7 \\ \hline \end{array}$ | $\begin{array}{r} 12 \\ \times\,6 \\ \hline \end{array}$ | $\begin{array}{r} 4 \\ +\,9 \\ \hline \end{array}$ | $\begin{array}{r} 2 \\ \times\,8 \\ \hline \end{array}$ | $\begin{array}{r} 12 \\ \times\,4 \\ \hline \end{array}$ | $\begin{array}{r} 11 \\ -\,6 \\ \hline \end{array}$ |

| 4. | $\begin{array}{r} 5 \\ \times\,7 \\ \hline \end{array}$ | $\begin{array}{r} 7 \\ +\,6 \\ \hline \end{array}$ | $\begin{array}{r} 12 \\ -\,8 \\ \hline \end{array}$ | $\begin{array}{r} 11 \\ \times\,10 \\ \hline \end{array}$ | $\begin{array}{r} 9 \\ \times\,9 \\ \hline \end{array}$ | $\begin{array}{r} 3 \\ +\,8 \\ \hline \end{array}$ | $\begin{array}{r} 10 \\ -\,6 \\ \hline \end{array}$ | $\begin{array}{r} 12 \\ \times\,9 \\ \hline \end{array}$ | $\begin{array}{r} 14 \\ -\,9 \\ \hline \end{array}$ |

| 5. | $\begin{array}{r} 9 \\ \times\,6 \\ \hline \end{array}$ | $\begin{array}{r} 16 \\ -\,8 \\ \hline \end{array}$ | $\begin{array}{r} 11 \\ \times\,12 \\ \hline \end{array}$ | $\begin{array}{r} 9 \\ -\,8 \\ \hline \end{array}$ | $\begin{array}{r} 4 \\ +\,5 \\ \hline \end{array}$ | $\begin{array}{r} 7 \\ +\,8 \\ \hline \end{array}$ | $\begin{array}{r} 6 \\ \times\,7 \\ \hline \end{array}$ | $\begin{array}{r} 13 \\ -\,9 \\ \hline \end{array}$ | $\begin{array}{r} 5 \\ -\,0 \\ \hline \end{array}$ |

6.

8	12	10	7	3	2	12	15	11
− 7	× 12	× 7	× 7	× 6	+ 9	− 3	− 9	× 5

7.

4	10	12	9	8	5	11	18	9
× 7	− 5	× 10	× 4	+ 8	× 5	− 9	− 9	+ 6

8.

3	15	17	7	5	8	10	9	14
× 4	− 7	− 8	× 8	× 6	× 6	× 11	+ 4	− 8

9. $8\overline{)48}$ $7\overline{)84}$ $6\overline{)24}$ $11\overline{)110}$ $12\overline{)72}$ $10\overline{)120}$

10. $7\overline{)56}$ $4\overline{)20}$ $3\overline{)9}$ $10\overline{)100}$ $11\overline{)121}$ $12\overline{)96}$

11. $9\overline{)36}$ $6\overline{)18}$ $5\overline{)40}$ $12\overline{)132}$ $10\overline{)110}$ $12\overline{)108}$

12. $7 \times \underline{\hspace{1cm}} = 35$ $\underline{\hspace{1cm}} \times 4 = 8$ $\underline{\hspace{1cm}} \times 5 = 60$ $9 \times \underline{\hspace{1cm}} = 27$

13. $8 \div \underline{\hspace{1cm}} = 2$ $72 \div \underline{\hspace{1cm}} = 9$ $\underline{\hspace{1cm}} \div 6 = 9$ $\underline{\hspace{1cm}} \div 3 = 6$

1 pt. each

Speed Drill 104

Name _____   **Score** _____

"Whatsoever thy hand findeth to do, do it with thy might."

(Ecclesiastes 9:10)

1. 1 century = _____ years

2. 1 decade = _____ years

3. 1 ton = _____ pounds

4. 1 pound = _____ ounces

5. 1 minute = _____ seconds

6. 1 yard = _____ inches

7. 1 bushel = _____ pecks

8. 1 quart = _____ pints

9. 4 yards = _____ feet

10. 2 quarts = _____ gallon

11. 24 inches = _____ feet

12. 3 weeks = _____ days

1 day = _____ hours

1 year = _____ days

1 year = _____ weeks

April = _____ days

December = _____ days

1 gallon = _____ quarts

1 pint = _____ cups

1 peck = _____ quarts

4 pints = _____ cups

4 pints = _____ quarts

$\frac{1}{4}$ hour = _____ minutes

$\frac{1}{4}$ pound = _____ ounces

4 pt. each

Speed Drill 106

"Whatsoever thy hand findeth to do, do it with thy might."

(Ecclesiastes 9:10)

1. 1 quarter, 3 dimes = _____ ¢

2. 2 quarters, 4 nickels = _____ ¢

3. 5 dimes, 3 nickels = _____ ¢

4. 2 dimes, 1 nickel, 7 pennies = _____ ¢

5. 1 half dollar, 1 quarter = _____ ¢

6. 7 quarters = $ _____

7. 12 dimes = $ _____

8. 3 quarters, 4 pennies = _____ ¢

9. 2 five-dollar bills, 3 one-dollar bills = $ _____

10. 2 twenty-dollar bills, 1 ten-dollar bill = $ _____

8 pt. each

Speed Drill 108

Name _____   Score _____

"Whatsoever thy hand findeth to do, do it with thy might."

(Ecclesiastes 9:10)

1. 1 dime = _____ nickels   1 dime = _____ pennies

2. 1 quarter = _____ nickels

3. 1 quarter = _____ dimes and one nickel

4. 1 quarter = one dime and _____ nickels

5. 1 quarter = two dimes and _____ pennies

6. 1 half dollar = _____ pennies   1 half dollar = _____ nickels

7. 1 half dollar = _____ dimes   1 half dollar = _____ quarters

8. 1 dollar = _____ quarters   1 dollar = _____ nickels

9. 1 dollar = _____ pennies   1 dollar = _____ dimes

10. 1 dollar = 2 quarters and _____ dimes

11. 1 dollar = 3 quarters and _____ nickels

12. 1 twenty-dollar bill = _____ five-dollar bills

13. 1 twenty-dollar bill = _____ ten-dollar bills

5 pt. each

Speed Drill 110

Name _____   **Score** _____

"Whatsoever thy hand findeth to do, do it with thy might."

(Ecclesiastes 9:10)

Do each step in the order given.

1. $6 \times 8 \div 12 \times 7 + 8 \div 3 =$ _____

2. $3 + 7 \times 3 \div 6 + 9 - 7 =$ _____

3. $16 \div 2 \times 7 - 14 \div 6 \times 3 =$ _____

4. $4 \times 6 \div 8 - 3 \times 5 + 11 =$ _____

5. $7 \times 5 - 3 \div 4 - 2 \times 9 =$ _____

6. $4 + 5 \div 3 \times 6 - 7 \times 12 =$ _____

7. $5 \times 3 - 6 \times 5 + 4 \div 7 + 6 =$ _____

8. $10 - 6 \times 5 \div 2 \times 4 \div 5 - 5 =$ _____

9 pt. each

Speed Drill 112

Name _____   Score _____

"Whatsoever thy hand findeth to do, do it with thy might."

(Ecclesiastes 9:10)

1. $6 + 7 =$ _____ $18 \div 3 =$ _____ $4 \times 9 =$ _____ $25 \div 5 =$ _____

2. $10 - 7 =$ _____ $8 + 9 =$ _____ $13 - 4 =$ _____ $7 \times 9 =$ _____

3. $8 \times 7 =$ _____ $35 \div 5 =$ _____ $9 \times 9 =$ _____ $8 + 6 =$ _____

4. $15 - 9 =$ _____ $9 - 6 =$ _____ $4 + 7 =$ _____ $2 + 8 =$ _____

5. $7 \times 3 =$ _____ $4 \div 4 =$ _____ $4 \times 4 =$ _____ $4 - 4 =$ _____

6. $11 \times 10 =$ _____ $3 \times 12 =$ _____ $8 + 4 =$ _____ $12 - 5 =$ _____

7. $30 \div 5 =$ _____ $72 \div 9 =$ _____ $9 - 4 =$ _____ $9 \times 3 =$ _____

8. $8 \times 8 =$ _____ $4 + 9 =$ _____ $14 - 8 =$ _____ $11 - 9 =$ _____

9. $48 \div 12 =$ _____ $3 \times 11 =$ _____ $3 + 9 =$ _____ $2 \times 12 =$ _____

10. $6 \times 6 =$ _____ $54 \div 9 =$ _____ $7 + 8 =$ _____ $16 - 8 =$ _____

2 pt. each

Speed Drill 114

Name _____   Score _____

"Whatsoever thy hand findeth to do, do it with thy might."

(Ecclesiastes 9:10)

1. $8 + \underline{\quad} = 12$ $\underline{\quad} \times 6 = 24$ $9 - \underline{\quad} = 6$ $20 \div \underline{\quad} = 5$

2. $\underline{\quad} - 4 = 7$ $5 + 9 = \underline{\quad}$ $\underline{\quad} \div 7 = 2$ $7 \times 6 = \underline{\quad}$

3. $11 \times \underline{\quad} = 121$ $15 \div \underline{\quad} = 5$ $\underline{\quad} - 8 = 9$ $\underline{\quad} \times 8 = 24$

4. $\underline{\quad} \div 4 = 3$ $\underline{\quad} + 6 = 12$ $15 - 7 = \underline{\quad}$ $3 + \underline{\quad} = 9$

5. $8 \times 5 = \underline{\quad}$ $12 \times 4 = \underline{\quad}$ $\underline{\quad} \div 6 = 8$ $\underline{\quad} \div 2 = 4$

6. $3 + \underline{\quad} = 7$ $\underline{\quad} \times 4 = 28$ $13 - \underline{\quad} = 7$ $9 + 9 = \underline{\quad}$

7. $\underline{\quad} \div 6 = 5$ $7 + \underline{\quad} = 16$ $4 \times 8 = \underline{\quad}$ $12 - \underline{\quad} = 3$

8. $10 - 4 = \underline{\quad}$ $72 \div \underline{\quad} = 6$ $\underline{\quad} - 6 = 2$ $\underline{\quad} \times 4 = 16$

3 pt. each

Speed Drill 116

Name _____   *Score* _____

"Whatsoever thy hand findeth to do, do it with thy might."

(Ecclesiastes 9:10)

1.

2,567	4,908	8,130	3,895
× 53	× 76	× 98	× 40

15 pt. each

Speed Drill 118

Name _____   *Score* _____

"Whatsoever thy hand findeth to do, do it with thy might."

(Ecclesiastes 9:10)

1. $\frac{1}{4}$ of 24 = _____ $\frac{1}{2}$ of 10 = _____ $\frac{1}{3}$ of 12 = _____

2. $\frac{1}{5}$ × 30 = _____ $\frac{1}{6}$ × 42 = _____ $\frac{1}{7}$ × 21 = _____

3. $\frac{3}{4}$ of 24 = _____ $\frac{2}{3}$ of 15 = _____ $\frac{2}{7}$ of 14 = _____

4. $\frac{5}{8}$ × 40 = _____ $\frac{3}{5}$ × 30 = _____ $\frac{5}{6}$ × 36 = _____

5. $\frac{3}{4}$ × 12 = _____ $\frac{4}{9}$ × 18 = _____ $\frac{2}{9}$ × 18 = _____

6. $1\frac{1}{2}$ × 12 = _____ $2\frac{1}{4}$ × 8 = _____ $1\frac{1}{3}$ × 9 = _____

7. $2\frac{1}{2}$ × 10 = _____ $3\frac{1}{3}$ × 6 = _____ $1\frac{1}{5}$ × 15 = _____

8. $1\frac{1}{8}$ × 24 = _____ $3\frac{1}{2}$ × 4 = _____ $3\frac{1}{8}$ × 8 = _____

3 pt. each

Speed Drill 120

Name _____   **Score** _____

"Whatsoever thy hand findeth to do, do it with thy might."

(Ecclesiastes 9:10)

1. $4\overline{)20}$ $3\overline{)21}$ $9\overline{)72}$ $4\overline{)36}$ $5\overline{)60}$ $12\overline{)48}$ $10\overline{)120}$

2. $6\overline{)36}$ $8\overline{)32}$ $2\overline{)24}$ $7\overline{)56}$ $4\overline{)36}$ $11\overline{)99}$ $12\overline{)132}$

3. $7\overline{)28}$ $4\overline{)16}$ $8\overline{)40}$ $8\overline{)64}$ $5\overline{)30}$ $9\overline{)54}$ $11\overline{)110}$

4. $3\overline{)15}$ $8\overline{)48}$ $4\overline{)12}$ $9\overline{)81}$ $6\overline{)18}$ $12\overline{)96}$ $10\overline{)100}$

5. $9\overline{)90}$ $5\overline{)45}$ $2\overline{)14}$ $7\overline{)42}$ $4\overline{)24}$ $6\overline{)72}$ $11\overline{)121}$

6. $4\overline{)28}$ $9\overline{)72}$ $8\overline{)56}$ $4\overline{)32}$ $4\overline{)8}$ $7\overline{)49}$ $12\overline{)60}$

7. $6\overline{)54}$ $5\overline{)25}$ $3\overline{)9}$ $3\overline{)27}$ $9\overline{)36}$ $10\overline{)60}$ $12\overline{)84}$

2 pt. each

Speed Drill 122

Name _____   **Score** _____

"Whatsoever thy hand findeth to do, do it with thy might."

(Ecclesiastes 9:10)

1.

```
   82
   45
   63
   36
 + 17
```

```
 8,946
 3,892
 5,173
+4,527
```

```
 6,010
-4,699
```

```
 9,500
-6,428
```

2.

```
  368
×   4
```

```
   57
 × 73
```

```
8)75
```

```
6)3,762
```

8 pt. each

Speed Drill 124

Name _____   **Score** _____

"Whatsoever thy hand findeth to do, do it with thy might."

(Ecclesiastes 9:10)

Underline the correct answers.

1. The answer to a subtraction problem is the (product, subtrahend, difference).

2. The answer to a division problem is the (divisor, dividend, quotient).

3. The answer to an addition problem is the (sum, addend, product).

4. The answer to a multiplication problem is the (multiplicand, product, quotient).

5. A number added in an addition problem is (an addend, a sum, a partial product).

6. The number being divided is the (divisor, dividend, quotient).

7. The number taken away is the (minuend, subtrahend).

8. The bottom number of a fraction is the (denominator, numerator).

9. A whole number and fraction together is called (a mixed number, a proper fraction, an improper fraction).

10. A fraction like $\frac{10}{8}$ is called (a mixed number, a proper fraction, an improper fraction).

10 pt. each

Speed Drill 126

Name _____   **Score** _____

"Whatsoever thy hand findeth to do, do it with thy might."

(Ecclesiastes 9:10)

Do each step in the order given.

1. $8 \times 3 - 6 \div 9 + 7 \times 9 = $ _____

2. $10 \div 2 \times 6 + 3 \div 11 \times 12 = $ _____

3. $6 \times 7 - 2 \div 5 \times 6 - 3 \div 5 = $ _____

4. $7 - 5 \times 6 \times 5 \div 10 + 9 - 8 = $ _____

5. $4 + 8 \div 3 \times 7 - 1 \div 3 \times 7 = $ _____

6. $11 - 8 \times 7 - 5 \div 4 + 20 \div 6 = $ _____

7. $8 \times 9 \div 6 \times 9 - 8 \div 10 \times 11 = $ _____

8. $5 + 4 \times 6 + 2 \div 7 \div 2 \times 8 - 3 = $ _____

9 pt. each

Speed Drill 128

Name _____   *Score* _____

"Whatsoever thy hand findeth to do, do it with thy might."

(Ecclesiastes 9:10)

A. Write the times shown on the clocks.

1. a.

    b.

    c.

    d.

    _____   _____   _____   _____

2. a.  b.  c.  d.

_____   _____   _____   _____

B. *Draw hands on the clocks to show the times given.*

3. a. 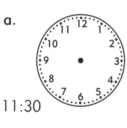 b. 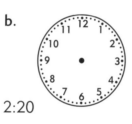 c. 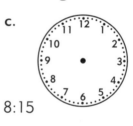 d.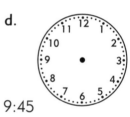

11:30   2:20   8:15   9:45

4. a. 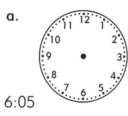 b. 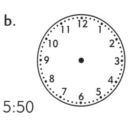 c. 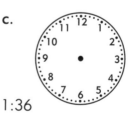 d.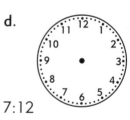

6:05   5:50   1:36   7:12

6 pt. each

Speed Drill 130

Name _____   **Score** _____

1. $\begin{array}{r} 6 \\ +\,4 \\ \hline \end{array}$ $\begin{array}{r} 7 \\ +\,2 \\ \hline \end{array}$ $\begin{array}{r} 3 \\ +\,1 \\ \hline \end{array}$ $\begin{array}{r} 1 \\ +\,7 \\ \hline \end{array}$ $\begin{array}{r} 9 \\ +\,8 \\ \hline \end{array}$ $\begin{array}{r} 3 \\ +\,4 \\ \hline \end{array}$ $\begin{array}{r} 5 \\ +\,5 \\ \hline \end{array}$ $\begin{array}{r} 9 \\ +\,2 \\ \hline \end{array}$ $\begin{array}{r} 2 \\ +\,4 \\ \hline \end{array}$

2. $\begin{array}{r} 2 \\ +\,2 \\ \hline \end{array}$ $\begin{array}{r} 1 \\ +\,5 \\ \hline \end{array}$ $\begin{array}{r} 9 \\ +\,7 \\ \hline \end{array}$ $\begin{array}{r} 4 \\ +\,4 \\ \hline \end{array}$ $\begin{array}{r} 6 \\ +\,7 \\ \hline \end{array}$ $\begin{array}{r} 8 \\ +\,5 \\ \hline \end{array}$ $\begin{array}{r} 1 \\ +\,2 \\ \hline \end{array}$ $\begin{array}{r} 8 \\ +\,4 \\ \hline \end{array}$ $\begin{array}{r} 7 \\ +\,3 \\ \hline \end{array}$

3. $\begin{array}{r} 8 \\ +\,8 \\ \hline \end{array}$ $\begin{array}{r} 6 \\ +\,3 \\ \hline \end{array}$ $\begin{array}{r} 9 \\ +\,1 \\ \hline \end{array}$ $\begin{array}{r} 2 \\ +\,3 \\ \hline \end{array}$ $\begin{array}{r} 4 \\ +\,9 \\ \hline \end{array}$ $\begin{array}{r} 5 \\ +\,3 \\ \hline \end{array}$ $\begin{array}{r} 9 \\ +\,3 \\ \hline \end{array}$ $\begin{array}{r} 6 \\ +\,6 \\ \hline \end{array}$ $\begin{array}{r} 2 \\ +\,8 \\ \hline \end{array}$

4. $\begin{array}{r} 9 \\ +\,5 \\ \hline \end{array}$ $\begin{array}{r} 7 \\ +\,4 \\ \hline \end{array}$ $\begin{array}{r} 4 \\ +\,1 \\ \hline \end{array}$ $\begin{array}{r} 1 \\ +\,6 \\ \hline \end{array}$ $\begin{array}{r} 8 \\ +\,3 \\ \hline \end{array}$ $\begin{array}{r} 6 \\ +\,5 \\ \hline \end{array}$ $\begin{array}{r} 3 \\ +\,3 \\ \hline \end{array}$ $\begin{array}{r} 2 \\ +\,6 \\ \hline \end{array}$ $\begin{array}{r} 9 \\ +\,4 \\ \hline \end{array}$

5.

5	3	7	1	3	4	8	5	4
$+\,2$	$+\,9$	$+\,7$	$+\,3$	$+\,7$	$+\,2$	$+\,1$	$+\,9$	$+\,5$

6.

1	5	7	3	2	1	8	9	4
$+\,1$	$+\,6$	$+\,5$	$+\,2$	$+\,1$	$+\,9$	$+\,6$	$+\,9$	$+\,7$

7.

6	1	7	5	3	2	1	7	3
$+\,1$	$+\,8$	$+\,6$	$+\,4$	$+\,6$	$+\,5$	$+\,4$	$+\,1$	$+\,8$

8.

2	9	6	7	5	4	5	8	6
$+\,7$	$+\,6$	$+\,8$	$+\,9$	$+\,1$	$+\,6$	$+\,7$	$+\,2$	$+\,9$

9.

4	6	2	8	3	8	5	7	4
$+\,3$	$+\,2$	$+\,9$	$+\,7$	$+\,5$	$+\,9$	$+\,8$	$+\,8$	$+\,8$

2 pt. each

Speed Drill 132

Name _____   **Score** _____

1.

$$\begin{array}{r} 4 \\ +\ 3 \\ \hline \end{array} \quad \begin{array}{r} 2 \\ +\ 7 \\ \hline \end{array} \quad \begin{array}{r} 6 \\ +\ 1 \\ \hline \end{array} \quad \begin{array}{r} 1 \\ +\ 1 \\ \hline \end{array} \quad \begin{array}{r} 5 \\ +\ 2 \\ \hline \end{array} \quad \begin{array}{r} 9 \\ +\ 5 \\ \hline \end{array} \quad \begin{array}{r} 8 \\ +\ 8 \\ \hline \end{array} \quad \begin{array}{r} 2 \\ +\ 2 \\ \hline \end{array} \quad \begin{array}{r} 6 \\ +\ 4 \\ \hline \end{array}$$

2.

$$\begin{array}{r} 1 \\ +\ 7 \\ \hline \end{array} \quad \begin{array}{r} 4 \\ +\ 4 \\ \hline \end{array} \quad \begin{array}{r} 2 \\ +\ 3 \\ \hline \end{array} \quad \begin{array}{r} 1 \\ +\ 6 \\ \hline \end{array} \quad \begin{array}{r} 1 \\ +\ 3 \\ \hline \end{array} \quad \begin{array}{r} 3 \\ +\ 2 \\ \hline \end{array} \quad \begin{array}{r} 5 \\ +\ 4 \\ \hline \end{array} \quad \begin{array}{r} 7 \\ +\ 9 \\ \hline \end{array} \quad \begin{array}{r} 8 \\ +\ 7 \\ \hline \end{array}$$

3.

$$\begin{array}{r} 7 \\ +\ 2 \\ \hline \end{array} \quad \begin{array}{r} 1 \\ +\ 5 \\ \hline \end{array} \quad \begin{array}{r} 6 \\ +\ 3 \\ \hline \end{array} \quad \begin{array}{r} 7 \\ +\ 4 \\ \hline \end{array} \quad \begin{array}{r} 3 \\ +\ 9 \\ \hline \end{array} \quad \begin{array}{r} 5 \\ +\ 6 \\ \hline \end{array} \quad \begin{array}{r} 1 \\ +\ 8 \\ \hline \end{array} \quad \begin{array}{r} 9 \\ +\ 6 \\ \hline \end{array} \quad \begin{array}{r} 6 \\ +\ 2 \\ \hline \end{array}$$

4.

$$\begin{array}{r} 3 \\ +\ 1 \\ \hline \end{array} \quad \begin{array}{r} 9 \\ +\ 7 \\ \hline \end{array} \quad \begin{array}{r} 9 \\ +\ 1 \\ \hline \end{array} \quad \begin{array}{r} 4 \\ +\ 1 \\ \hline \end{array} \quad \begin{array}{r} 7 \\ +\ 7 \\ \hline \end{array} \quad \begin{array}{r} 7 \\ +\ 5 \\ \hline \end{array} \quad \begin{array}{r} 7 \\ +\ 6 \\ \hline \end{array} \quad \begin{array}{r} 6 \\ +\ 8 \\ \hline \end{array} \quad \begin{array}{r} 2 \\ +\ 9 \\ \hline \end{array}$$

5.

2 + 4	7 + 3	2 + 8	9 + 4	4 + 5	4 + 7	3 + 8	6 + 9	4 + 8

6.

3 + 5	5 + 1	3 + 6	2 + 1	3 + 7	8 + 3	4 + 9	6 + 7	9 + 8

7.

5 + 5	1 + 2	9 + 3	3 + 3	8 + 1	8 + 6	1 + 4	5 + 7	5 + 8

8.

9 + 2	8 + 4	6 + 6	2 + 6	5 + 9	9 + 9	7 + 1	8 + 2	7 + 8

9.

3 + 4	8 + 5	5 + 3	6 + 5	4 + 2	1 + 9	2 + 5	4 + 6	8 + 9

2 pt. each

Speed Drill 134

Name _____ **Score** _____

"Whatsoever thy hand findeth to do, do it with thy might."

(Ecclesiastes 9:10)

1.

5	8	4	9	2	7
4	6	1	5	7	8
3	5	6	6	3	4
5	3	9	5	4	7
+ 7	+ 8	+ 7	+ 5	+ 8	+ 7

2.

3	1	9	5	6	9
5	6	4	7	8	9
2	6	5	3	4	6
1	5	1	5	7	3
+ 8	+ 4	+ 7	+ 8	+ 9	+ 6

6 pt. each

Speed Drill 136

Name _____   **Score** _____

"Whatsoever thy hand findeth to do, do it with thy might."

(Ecclesiastes 9:10)

A. Write the correct numbers in the blanks.

1. 1 bushel = _____ pecks   1 yd. = _____ in.   1 mile = _____ feet
2. 1 year = _____ days   1 hr. = _____ min.   1 gallon = _____ quarts
3. 1 century = _____ years   1 qt. = _____ pt.   1 day = _____ hours
4. 1 ton = _____ pounds   1 lb.= _____ oz.   1 year = _____ weeks
5. 1 peck = _____ quarts   1 ft. = _____ in.   1 year = _____ months
6. 1 pint = _____ cups   1 yd. = _____ ft.   1 dozen = _____ items
7. 3 quarts = _____ cups   12 ft. = _____ yd.   30 minutes = _____ hour
8. 36 eggs = _____ dozen   4 ft. = _____ in.   3 cups = _____ pints

B. Draw lines to match.

9.   a. 1,000   hecto-   g. meter   unit of weight
     b. 100   kilo-   h. liter   unit of length
     c. 10   centi-   i. gram   unit of liquid capacity
     d. 0.1   deka-
     e. 0.01   deci-
     f. 0.001   milli-

3 pt. each

Speed Drill 138

1.
$$
\begin{array}{r} 4 \\ \times\,3 \\ \hline \end{array}
\quad
\begin{array}{r} 2 \\ \times\,7 \\ \hline \end{array}
\quad
\begin{array}{r} 12 \\ \times\,6 \\ \hline \end{array}
\quad
\begin{array}{r} 1 \\ \times\,1 \\ \hline \end{array}
\quad
\begin{array}{r} 5 \\ \times\,2 \\ \hline \end{array}
\quad
\begin{array}{r} 9 \\ \times\,5 \\ \hline \end{array}
\quad
\begin{array}{r} 8 \\ \times\,8 \\ \hline \end{array}
\quad
\begin{array}{r} 2 \\ \times\,2 \\ \hline \end{array}
\quad
\begin{array}{r} 6 \\ \times\,4 \\ \hline \end{array}
$$

2.
$$
\begin{array}{r} 11 \\ \times\,7 \\ \hline \end{array}
\quad
\begin{array}{r} 4 \\ \times\,4 \\ \hline \end{array}
\quad
\begin{array}{r} 2 \\ \times\,3 \\ \hline \end{array}
\quad
\begin{array}{r} 10 \\ \times\,6 \\ \hline \end{array}
\quad
\begin{array}{r} 12 \\ \times\,3 \\ \hline \end{array}
\quad
\begin{array}{r} 3 \\ \times\,2 \\ \hline \end{array}
\quad
\begin{array}{r} 5 \\ \times\,4 \\ \hline \end{array}
\quad
\begin{array}{r} 7 \\ \times\,9 \\ \hline \end{array}
\quad
\begin{array}{r} 8 \\ \times\,7 \\ \hline \end{array}
$$

3.
$$
\begin{array}{r} 7 \\ \times\,2 \\ \hline \end{array}
\quad
\begin{array}{r} 12 \\ \times\,5 \\ \hline \end{array}
\quad
\begin{array}{r} 6 \\ \times\,3 \\ \hline \end{array}
\quad
\begin{array}{r} 7 \\ \times\,4 \\ \hline \end{array}
\quad
\begin{array}{r} 3 \\ \times\,9 \\ \hline \end{array}
\quad
\begin{array}{r} 5 \\ \times\,6 \\ \hline \end{array}
\quad
\begin{array}{r} 12 \\ \times\,8 \\ \hline \end{array}
\quad
\begin{array}{r} 9 \\ \times\,6 \\ \hline \end{array}
\quad
\begin{array}{r} 6 \\ \times\,2 \\ \hline \end{array}
$$

4.
$$
\begin{array}{r} 12 \\ \times\,12 \\ \hline \end{array}
\quad
\begin{array}{r} 9 \\ \times\,7 \\ \hline \end{array}
\quad
\begin{array}{r} 12 \\ \times\,9 \\ \hline \end{array}
\quad
\begin{array}{r} 4 \\ \times\,1 \\ \hline \end{array}
\quad
\begin{array}{r} 7 \\ \times\,7 \\ \hline \end{array}
\quad
\begin{array}{r} 7 \\ \times\,5 \\ \hline \end{array}
\quad
\begin{array}{r} 7 \\ \times\,6 \\ \hline \end{array}
\quad
\begin{array}{r} 6 \\ \times\,8 \\ \hline \end{array}
\quad
\begin{array}{r} 2 \\ \times\,9 \\ \hline \end{array}
$$

5.

2	7	2	9	4	4	3	6	4
× 4	× 3	× 8	× 4	× 5	× 7	× 8	× 9	× 8

6.

3	12	3	10	3	8	4	6	9
× 5	× 11	× 6	× 2	× 7	× 3	× 9	× 7	× 8

7.

5	12	9	3	10	8	11	5	5
× 5	× 2	× 3	× 3	× 11	× 6	× 11	× 7	× 8

8.

9	8	6	2	5	9	12	8	7
× 2	× 4	× 6	× 6	× 9	× 9	× 7	× 2	× 8

9.

3	8	5	6	4	12	2	4	8
× 4	× 5	× 3	× 5	× 2	× 9	× 5	× 6	× 9

2 pt. each

Speed Drill 140

1.

6	7	3	10	9	3	5	9	2
× 4	× 2	× 1	× 7	× 8	× 4	× 5	× 2	× 4

2.

2	11	9	4	6	8	12	8	7
× 2	× 5	× 7	× 4	× 7	× 5	× 2	× 4	× 3

3.

8	6	11	2	4	5	9	6	2
× 8	× 3	× 9	× 3	× 9	× 3	× 3	× 6	× 8

4.

9	7	12	12	8	6	3	2	9
× 5	× 4	× 4	× 6	× 3	× 5	× 3	× 6	× 4

5.

| $\begin{array}{r} 5 \\ \times\,2 \\ \hline \end{array}$ | $\begin{array}{r} 3 \\ \times\,9 \\ \hline \end{array}$ | $\begin{array}{r} 7 \\ \times\,7 \\ \hline \end{array}$ | $\begin{array}{r} 10 \\ \times\,3 \\ \hline \end{array}$ | $\begin{array}{r} 3 \\ \times\,7 \\ \hline \end{array}$ | $\begin{array}{r} 4 \\ \times\,2 \\ \hline \end{array}$ | $\begin{array}{r} 12 \\ \times\,8 \\ \hline \end{array}$ | $\begin{array}{r} 5 \\ \times\,9 \\ \hline \end{array}$ | $\begin{array}{r} 4 \\ \times\,5 \\ \hline \end{array}$ |

6.

| $\begin{array}{r} 12 \\ \times\,9 \\ \hline \end{array}$ | $\begin{array}{r} 5 \\ \times\,6 \\ \hline \end{array}$ | $\begin{array}{r} 7 \\ \times\,5 \\ \hline \end{array}$ | $\begin{array}{r} 3 \\ \times\,2 \\ \hline \end{array}$ | $\begin{array}{r} 12 \\ \times\,12 \\ \hline \end{array}$ | $\begin{array}{r} 11 \\ \times\,12 \\ \hline \end{array}$ | $\begin{array}{r} 8 \\ \times\,6 \\ \hline \end{array}$ | $\begin{array}{r} 9 \\ \times\,9 \\ \hline \end{array}$ | $\begin{array}{r} 4 \\ \times\,7 \\ \hline \end{array}$ |

7.

| $\begin{array}{r} 6 \\ \times\,1 \\ \hline \end{array}$ | $\begin{array}{r} 10 \\ \times\,10 \\ \hline \end{array}$ | $\begin{array}{r} 7 \\ \times\,6 \\ \hline \end{array}$ | $\begin{array}{r} 5 \\ \times\,4 \\ \hline \end{array}$ | $\begin{array}{r} 3 \\ \times\,6 \\ \hline \end{array}$ | $\begin{array}{r} 2 \\ \times\,5 \\ \hline \end{array}$ | $\begin{array}{r} 11 \\ \times\,11 \\ \hline \end{array}$ | $\begin{array}{r} 7 \\ \times\,1 \\ \hline \end{array}$ | $\begin{array}{r} 3 \\ \times\,8 \\ \hline \end{array}$ |

8.

| $\begin{array}{r} 2 \\ \times\,7 \\ \hline \end{array}$ | $\begin{array}{r} 9 \\ \times\,6 \\ \hline \end{array}$ | $\begin{array}{r} 6 \\ \times\,8 \\ \hline \end{array}$ | $\begin{array}{r} 7 \\ \times\,9 \\ \hline \end{array}$ | $\begin{array}{r} 12 \\ \times\,5 \\ \hline \end{array}$ | $\begin{array}{r} 4 \\ \times\,6 \\ \hline \end{array}$ | $\begin{array}{r} 5 \\ \times\,7 \\ \hline \end{array}$ | $\begin{array}{r} 8 \\ \times\,2 \\ \hline \end{array}$ | $\begin{array}{r} 6 \\ \times\,9 \\ \hline \end{array}$ |

9.

| $\begin{array}{r} 4 \\ \times\,3 \\ \hline \end{array}$ | $\begin{array}{r} 6 \\ \times\,2 \\ \hline \end{array}$ | $\begin{array}{r} 2 \\ \times\,9 \\ \hline \end{array}$ | $\begin{array}{r} 8 \\ \times\,7 \\ \hline \end{array}$ | $\begin{array}{r} 3 \\ \times\,5 \\ \hline \end{array}$ | $\begin{array}{r} 8 \\ \times\,9 \\ \hline \end{array}$ | $\begin{array}{r} 5 \\ \times\,8 \\ \hline \end{array}$ | $\begin{array}{r} 7 \\ \times\,8 \\ \hline \end{array}$ | $\begin{array}{r} 4 \\ \times\,8 \\ \hline \end{array}$ |

2 pt. each

Speed Drill 142

Name _____   **Score** _____

"Whatsoever thy hand findeth to do, do it with thy might."

(Ecclesiastes 9:10)

1. $6\overline{)24}$ $3\overline{)18}$ $2\overline{)14}$ $5\overline{)25}$ $8\overline{)72}$ $10\overline{)50}$ $12\overline{)120}$

2. $4\overline{)16}$ $9\overline{)45}$ $3\overline{)15}$ $1\overline{)8}$ $3\overline{)27}$ $11\overline{)88}$ $12\overline{)108}$

3. $5\overline{)40}$ $4\overline{)32}$ $6\overline{)42}$ $8\overline{)40}$ $2\overline{)22}$ $12\overline{)12}$ $10\overline{)100}$

4. $8\overline{)64}$ $2\overline{)10}$ $8\overline{)24}$ $7\overline{)49}$ $4\overline{)48}$ $11\overline{)33}$ $11\overline{)132}$

5. $1\overline{)5}$ $3\overline{)9}$ $4\overline{)20}$ $6\overline{)54}$ $3\overline{)21}$ $10\overline{)60}$ $11\overline{)121}$

6. $7\overline{)56}$ $2\overline{)8}$ $7\overline{)35}$ $9\overline{)63}$ $9\overline{)18}$ $12\overline{)24}$ $11\overline{)110}$

7. $4\overline{)36}$ $8\overline{)88}$ $2\overline{)6}$ $5\overline{)5}$ $7\overline{)14}$ $9\overline{)54}$ $10\overline{)120}$

8. $2\overline{)12}$ $3\overline{)12}$ $6\overline{)48}$ $9\overline{)81}$ $4\overline{)28}$ $10\overline{)40}$ $12\overline{)84}$

9. $7\overline{)63}$ $2\overline{)18}$ $1\overline{)10}$ $9\overline{)27}$ $5\overline{)30}$ $5\overline{)45}$ $12\overline{)60}$

10. $8\overline{)56}$ $5\overline{)10}$ $6\overline{)36}$ $7\overline{)28}$ $2\overline{)4}$ $11\overline{)66}$ $12\overline{)144}$

11. $7\overline{)21}$ $4\overline{)40}$ $8\overline{)96}$ $3\overline{)36}$ $3\overline{)24}$ $12\overline{)72}$ $10\overline{)110}$

2 pt. each

Speed Drill 144

Name _____   **Score** _____

"Whatsoever thy hand findeth to do, do it with thy might."

(Ecclesiastes 9:10)

1. $1\overline{)4}$ $8\overline{)16}$ $2\overline{)16}$ $4\overline{)16}$ $7\overline{)42}$ $10\overline{)80}$ $12\overline{)144}$

2. $3\overline{)24}$ $4\overline{)12}$ $9\overline{)36}$ $5\overline{)15}$ $4\overline{)40}$ $11\overline{)77}$ $10\overline{)110}$

3. $3\overline{)6}$ $9\overline{)72}$ $5\overline{)55}$ $3\overline{)36}$ $4\overline{)24}$ $10\overline{)30}$ $12\overline{)132}$

4. $5\overline{)35}$ $8\overline{)32}$ $1\overline{)6}$ $8\overline{)48}$ $4\overline{)8}$ $12\overline{)48}$ $11\overline{)121}$

5. $6\overline{)12}$ $6\overline{)30}$ $5\overline{)25}$ $6\overline{)18}$ $5\overline{)20}$ $12\overline{)72}$ $9\overline{)108}$

6. $8\overline{)96}$ $9\overline{)54}$ $7\overline{)42}$ $6\overline{)36}$ $4\overline{)36}$ $11\overline{)44}$ $10\overline{)100}$

7. $1\overline{)3}$ $6\overline{)72}$ $2\overline{)24}$ $8\overline{)24}$ $9\overline{)27}$ $7\overline{)49}$ $12\overline{)108}$

8. $3\overline{)18}$ $3\overline{)27}$ $4\overline{)32}$ $7\overline{)84}$ $9\overline{)9}$ $11\overline{)55}$ $9\overline{)99}$

9. $5\overline{)60}$ $3\overline{)33}$ $6\overline{)60}$ $8\overline{)56}$ $6\overline{)42}$ $10\overline{)10}$ $12\overline{)96}$

10. $3\overline{)21}$ $8\overline{)64}$ $7\overline{)28}$ $9\overline{)81}$ $2\overline{)24}$ $11\overline{)22}$ $11\overline{)110}$

11. $2\overline{)18}$ $6\overline{)18}$ $3\overline{)9}$ $6\overline{)6}$ $8\overline{)72}$ $12\overline{)36}$ $7\overline{)63}$

2 pt. each

Speed Drill 146

Name _____   Score _____

"Whatsoever thy hand findeth to do, do it with thy might."

(Ecclesiastes 9:10)

A. *Reduce these fractions to lowest terms.*

1. $\dfrac{12}{40}$ $\dfrac{6}{18}$ $\dfrac{10}{20}$ $\dfrac{8}{28}$ $\dfrac{9}{24}$ $\dfrac{10}{16}$

B. *Change to whole numbers or mixed numbers in simplest form.*

2. $\dfrac{7}{2}$ $\dfrac{8}{3}$ $\dfrac{10}{2}$ $\dfrac{10}{4}$ $\dfrac{13}{6}$ $\dfrac{9}{5}$

C. *Change to simpest form.*

3. $1\frac{4}{4}$ $2\frac{3}{2}$ $1\frac{15}{12}$ $3\frac{10}{8}$

6 pt. each

Speed Drill 148

"Whatsoever thy hand findeth to do, do it with thy might."

(Ecclesiastes 9:10)

Use your ruler for this drill.

1. Count by eighths. Fill in the missing numbers.

   ___   ___   ___   ___   ___   ___   ___   _1_   ___   ___   ___

2. Count by sixteenths. Fill in the missing numbers.

   ___   ___   ___   ___   ___   ___   ___   ___   ___

   ___   ___   ___   ___   ___   _1_

3. Write the measurement of each line in English units.

   _____   a.   _____

   _____   b.   _____

   _____   c.   _____

   _____   d.   _____

3 pt. each

Speed Drill 150

Name _____   **Score** _____

1.

8	10	5	11	13	4	6	12	10
− 6	− 5	− 1	− 4	− 8	− 4	− 3	− 3	− 7

2.

14	6	8	3	1	7	11	15	9
− 7	− 4	− 7	− 3	− 1	− 4	− 9	− 7	− 4

3.

12	16	9	7	8	5	10	13	9
− 8	− 8	− 7	− 2	− 1	− 3	− 4	− 6	− 6

4.

7	6	12	15	18	10	9	8	14
− 6	− 2	− 5	− 9	− 9	− 2	− 8	− 3	− 5

5.

17	13	10	9	7	5	2	16	11
− 8	− 4	− 1	− 3	− 5	− 5	− 1	− 7	− 3

6.

11	10	14	15	9	7	11	4	3
− 7	− 3	− 8	− 6	− 9	− 3	− 5	− 2	− 1

7.

13	11	8	6	4	17	11	8	5
− 7	− 2	− 4	− 5	− 3	− 9	− 8	− 5	− 2

8.

7	6	12	14	10	9	15	12	8
− 7	− 1	− 4	− 9	− 6	− 2	− 8	− 6	− 2

9.

16	13	10	12	14	10	13	12	11
− 9	− 5	− 9	− 7	− 6	− 8	− 9	− 9	− 6

2 pt. each

Speed Drill 152

1.

8	11	5	3	11	14	9	9	10
− 2	− 6	− 2	− 2	− 3	− 5	− 6	− 4	− 7

2.

8	14	12	7	17	11	13	7	16
− 6	− 7	− 8	− 6	− 8	− 7	− 7	− 1	− 9

3.

10	6	16	6	13	10	11	6	13
− 5	− 4	− 8	− 2	− 4	− 3	− 2	− 6	− 5

4.

5	8	9	12	10	14	8	12	10
− 4	− 7	− 7	− 5	− 1	− 8	− 4	− 4	− 9

5.

11	3	7	15	9	15	6	14	12
− 4	− 3	− 2	− 9	− 3	− 6	− 5	− 9	− 7

6.

13	1	8	18	7	9	4	10	14
− 8	− 0	− 8	− 9	− 5	− 1	− 1	− 6	− 6

7.

4	7	5	10	5	7	17	9	10
− 3	− 4	− 3	− 2	− 0	− 3	− 9	− 2	− 8

8.

12	15	13	8	16	4	8	12	12
− 6	− 7	− 6	− 3	− 7	− 2	− 5	− 3	− 9

9.

6	11	10	9	2	11	11	15	13
− 3	− 9	− 4	− 8	− 2	− 5	− 8	− 8	− 9

2 pt. each

Speed Drill 154

"Whatsoever thy hand findeth to do, do it with thy might."

(Ecclesiastes 9:10)

Do each step in the order given.

1. $8 \times 7 + 4 = $ _____ $5 \times 7 + 5 = $ _____ $7 \times 6 + 2 = $ _____

2. $5 \times 9 + 6 = $ _____ $8 \times 3 + 6 = $ _____ $4 \times 4 + 7 = $ _____

3. $4 \times 8 + 5 = $ _____ $4 \times 6 + 5 = $ _____ $5 \times 8 + 3 = $ _____

4. $3 \times 9 + 4 = $ _____ $8 \times 8 + 4 = $ _____ $8 \times 9 + 6 = $ _____

5. $7 \times 9 + 3 = $ _____ $3 \times 7 + 2 = $ _____ $9 \times 4 + 5 = $ _____

6. $9 \times 9 + 7 \div 8 - 4 \times 8 = $ _____

7. $7 + 5 \times 6 - 2 \div 10 - 5 = $ _____

8. $8 \times 4 - 5 \div 3 + 2 + 12 = $ _____

5 pt. each

Speed Drill 156

Name _____   Score _____

"Whatsoever thy hand findeth to do, do it with thy might."

(Ecclesiastes 9:10)

1. $4 \times 9 =$ _____	$8 + 7 =$ _____	$28 \div 4 =$ _____	$13 - 6 =$ _____
2. $12 \times 10 =$ _____	$9 - 8 =$ _____	$7 \times 9 =$ _____	$9 + 4 =$ _____
3. $35 \div 5 =$ _____	$6 + 5 =$ _____	$42 \div 6 =$ _____	$12 - 7 =$ _____
4. $8 \times 6 =$ _____	$10 - 4 =$ _____	$48 \div 12 =$ _____	$8 + 4 =$ _____
5. $7 + 9 =$ _____	$18 \div 6 =$ _____	$11 - 5 =$ _____	$6 \times 5 =$ _____
6. $8 - 5 =$ _____	$7 \times 4 =$ _____	$8 + 3 =$ _____	$40 \div 5 =$ _____
7. $72 \div 9 =$ _____	$6 + 4 =$ _____	$3 \times 9 =$ _____	$18 - 9 =$ _____
8. $2 \times 8 =$ _____	$54 \div 6 =$ _____	$14 - 6 =$ _____	$5 + 9 =$ _____
9. $8 + 9 =$ _____	$8 \times 12 =$ _____	$21 \div 3 =$ _____	$9 - 4 =$ _____
10. $15 \div 3 =$ _____	$12 - 6 =$ _____	$11 \times 11 =$ _____	$7 + 7 =$ _____
11. $12 \times 12 =$ _____	$6 + 9 =$ _____	$16 - 8 =$ _____	$48 \div 6 =$ _____
12. $11 - 7 =$ _____	$60 \div 6 =$ _____	$5 + 8 =$ _____	$7 \times 8 =$ _____

2 pt. each

Speed Drill 158

Name _____   Score _____

"Whatsoever thy hand findeth to do, do it with thy might."

(Ecclesiastes 9:10)

A. Write numerals for these number words.

1. three hundred twenty-five billion _____

2. forty-six billion, two hundred million, fourteen _____

3. twelve billion, thirty-eight thousand _____

4. one hundred one billion, one hundred ten million, eleven thousand, one hundred

   _____

5. 8 billion, 18 million, 8 thousand, 88 _____

6. seven hundred ninety-four million _____

B. Write as Arabic numerals.

9. XL _____   MMCCIX _____   DCCLXVIII _____   XCIV _____

10 pt. each

Speed Drill 160

Name _____   Score _____

"Whatsoever thy hand findeth to do, do it with thy might."

(Ecclesiastes 9:10)

A. Write the missing numbers.

1. 1 day = _____ hours   1 year = _____ weeks   1 decade = _____ years

2. 1 meter = _____ cm   1 liter = _____ ml   1 kilogram = _____ grams

3. 1 year = _____ days   1 bushel = _____ pecks   1 quart = _____ cups

4. 1 yard = _____ feet   1 pound = _____ ounces   1 mile = _____ feet

5. 1 minute = _____ sec.   1 yard = _____ inches   1 ton = _____ pounds

6. 4 inches = _____ ft.   4 feet = _____ in.   4 yards = _____ ft.

7. 4 quarts = _____ pt.   4 quarts = _____ gal.   4 quarts = _____ cups

8. 4 meters = _____ cm   4 meters = _____ mm   4 cm = _____ mm

B. Write 1,000, 100, 10, 0.1, 0.01, or 0.001 after each prefix.

9. centi- _____   hecto- _____   kilo- _____

10. milli- _____   deci- _____   deka- _____

3 pt. each

Speed Drill 162

Name _____   Score _____

"Whatsoever thy hand findeth to do, do it with thy might."

(Ecclesiastes 9:10)

Write all answers in simplest form.

1.

$$\frac{5}{8}$$
$$+ \frac{3}{4}$$

$$\frac{7}{16}$$
$$\frac{1}{2}$$
$$+ \frac{3}{8}$$

$$\frac{8}{9}$$
$$- \frac{2}{3}$$

$$\frac{3}{4}$$
$$- \frac{5}{12}$$

2.

$$3\frac{1}{2}$$
$$+ 2\frac{1}{5}$$

$$1\frac{5}{8}$$
$$+ 1\frac{7}{8}$$

$$6$$
$$- 3\frac{2}{3}$$

$$4\frac{1}{2}$$
$$- 2\frac{7}{8}$$

8 pt. each

Speed Drill 164

Name _____   **Score** _____

"Whatsoever thy hand findeth to do, do it with thy might."

(Ecclesiastes 9:10)

A. *Write four number facts, using these sets of numbers.*

1. 12, 8, 4 _____ _____ _____ _____

2. 27, 9, 3 _____ _____ _____ _____

B. *Write the missing numbers to complete these number facts.*

3. $8 \times$ ____ $= 24$ ____ $- 6 = 4$ $9 +$ ____ $= 15$ ____ $\times 7 = 28$

4. $13 -$ ____ $= 7$ $64 \div$ ____ $= 8$ ____ $\div 5 = 9$ $8 + 6 =$ ____

5. ____ $+ 4 = 9$ $8 \times 4 =$ ____   ____ $- 7 = 5$ $42 \div$ ____ $= 7$

6. ____ $\times 6 = 30$ ____ $\div 2 = 4$ $7 +$ ____ $= 10$ $18 -$ ____ $= 9$

7. $56 \div 7 =$ ____   ____ $+ 6 = 11$ ____ $\times 6 = 36$ ____ $- 5 = 2$

8. $4 +$ ____ $= 11$ $8 -$ ____ $= 6$ $21 \div$ ____ $= 3$ $9 \times$ ____ $= 54$

9. ____ $\times 5 = 60$ $7 + 9 =$ ____ $13 - 9 =$ ____   ____ $\div 5 = 5$

10. $10 -$ ____ $= 2$ $7 \div$ ____ $= 7$ ____ $\times 7 = 49$ $8 +$ ____ $= 13$

2 pt. each

Speed Drill 166

Name _____   **Score** _____

"Whatsoever thy hand findeth to do, do it with thy might."

(Ecclesiastes 9:10)

Write the answers only.

1. $10 \times 68 = $ _____ $100 \times 317 = $ _____ $1{,}000 \times 45 = $ _____

2. $10 \times 780 = $ _____ $230 \div 10 = $ _____ $5 \times 70 = $ _____

3. $3 \times 16 = $ _____ $4 \times 28 = $ _____ $20 + 8 = $ _____

4. $30 + 5 = $ _____ $10 + 24 = $ _____ $12 + 13 = $ _____

5. $30 + 40 = $ _____ $16 + 4 = $ _____ $25 + 7 = $ _____

6. $18 + 13 = $ _____ $18 - 6 = $ _____ $16 - 5 = $ _____

7. $60 - 40 = $ _____ $26 - 10 = $ _____ $37 - 7 = $ _____

8. $25 - 12 = $ _____ $31 - 6 = $ _____ $20 - 4 = $ _____

4 pt. each

Speed Drill 168

Name _____   **Score** _____

"Whatsoever thy hand findeth to do, do it with thy might."

(Ecclesiastes 9:10)

1.
```
   26
   73
   48
   15
 + 61
```
```
  92,306
  15,864
+ 76,893
```
```
  5,020
- 3,489
```
```
  74,803
- 27,435
```

2.
```
 5,068
×    6
```
```
   843
× 708
```
```
6)1,488
```
```
32)1,728
```

8 pt. each